INTERNATIONAL SERIES OF MONOGRAPHS ON

ANALYTICAL CHEMISTRY

GENERAL EDITORS: R. BELCHER AND L. GORDON

Volume 4

PHOTOMETRIC TITRATIONS

A

OTHER TITLES IN THE SERIES ON ANALYTICAL CHEMISTRY

Vol. 1. WEISZ—*Microanalysis by the Ring Oven Technique*

Vol. 2. CROUTHAMEL (Ed.)—*Applied Gamma-ray Spectrometry*

Vol. 3. VICKERY—*The Analytical Chemistry of the Rare Earths*

PHOTOMETRIC TITRATIONS

by

J. B. HEADRIDGE, Ph.D. (Edin.)
Department of Chemistry
University of Sheffield

PERGAMON PRESS
NEW YORK · OXFORD · LONDON · PARIS
1961

PERGAMON PRESS INC.
122 East 55th Street, New York 22, N.Y.
Statler Center 640, 900 Wilshire Boulevard
Los Angeles 17, California
1404 New York Avenue N.W., Washington 5, D.C.

PERGAMON PRESS LTD.
Headington Hill Hall, Oxford
4 and 5 Fitzroy Square, London, W.1

PERGAMON PRESS S.A.R.L.
24 Rue des Ecoles, Paris Ve

PERGAMON PRESS G.m.b.H.
Kaiserstrasse 75, Frankfurt am Main

Library of Congress Card Number 61–14040

Set in Times New Roman 10/12 pt and Printed in Great Britain by
CHORLEY & PICKERSGILL LTD
Leeds and London

PREFACE

In this monograph an attempt has been made to collect together the widely scattered information pertaining to photometric titrations. I have deliberately refrained from listing every reference to this technique, since much of the work undertaken before World War II is no longer of interest because of the introduction of superior post-war instruments, and since, in my opinion, some of the papers published since the war have dealt with systems where a quicker visual end-point would have been as satisfactory. However, every effort has been made to present all the information on photometric titrations which may prove useful today.

In the chapter on "Precipitation Reactions", I have been briefer than I had originally intended since Bobtelsky, the chief worker in the field at present, has recently written a book on heterometry, which is another name for precipitation titrations, and he describes adequately much of the work in that field.

I acknowledge gratefully the assistance given to me by Mr. J. P. Candlin, who read the whole manuscript and suggested several changes which were later incorporated in the text. I express my thanks to Miss H. S. J. Clark for re-drawing the figures and to Messrs. E. J. Dixon and M. S. Taylor for their help in reading the proofs.

Sheffield
June, 1961

J. B. HEADRIDGE

CONTENTS

CHAPTER 1

INTRODUCTION AND THEORY

1.1 In photometric titrations the property studied in order to obtain the titration equivalence point is the optical density of the solution. For monochromatic light passing through a solution, the Lambert–Beer Law states that

$$\text{optical density} = \log \frac{I_0}{I} = kcd$$

where I_0 is the intensity of the incident light, I that of the transmitted light, k is a constant (the absorption or extinction coefficient), c is the concentration of the absorbing species and d is the length of the light path. Since photometric titrations are carried out in a vessel, for which the length of the light path is constant, the method is based on the simple relationship that the optical density is directly proportional to the concentration of the absorbing species. Changes occur in the concentration of the absorbing species and hence in the optical density of the solution, during the course of a titration, and by interpreting these changes the end-point is obtained. In most photometric titrations, a plot is drawn of optical density against volume of titrant added, and a study of such a plot gives the end-point.

Now clearly it is a complete waste of time to perform a photometric titration if a visual titration is satisfactory. The eye can readily detect sharp colour changes or marked changes in colour intensity. Photometric titration finds its use in systems where there is a gradual change in colour in the vicinity of the equivalence point or, in many cases, throughout the whole course of the titration. The technique may also be employed to detect the end-point in dark coloured solutions. In these cases a definite but very slight change in colour intensity usually occurs exactly at the equivalence point, but because of the dark colour of the solution the eye is not sensitive enough to detect this change in colour, which can, however, be readily distinguished with a photometer[1].

The great superiority of a spectrophotometer compared with th human eye in distinguishing very slight changes in the optica density of a solution has been demonstrated by Lane and Fritz[2], wh were able to titrate spectrophotometrically a $7 \cdot 5 \times 10^{-7}$ M solutio of neodymium with 10^{-5} M EDTA, where the solutions were s dilute that the differences in colour before and after the titratio were hardly discernible to the eye.

Photometric titrations may also, of course, be carried out in th ultra-violet and very near infra-red regions of the spectrum.

Finally, photometric detection of end-point may be employe in automatic titrations. Here a sharp change in colour intensit often occurs at the equivalence point. This could readily be detecte by eye and the titration terminated manually, but in the automati procedure the sharp change in optical density of the solution i used to operate a relay, and the addition of titrant to the solutio immediately ceases at the end-point.

1.2 Historical background. The first photometric titration using a conventional-type photometer were performed by Mülle and Partridge[3] in 1928. They used the change in photocell curren at the end-point to operate a relay and terminate the flow of titran from a burette. When automatic methods are only now becomin popular, it is sobering to reflect that more than thirty years ago completely satisfactory method for terminating a titration auto matically was available.

In the years from 1928 until shortly after World War II, abou fifty papers appeared on photometric titrations. These were per formed with laboratory-built filter photometers. It is known that photometric titration only provides the maximum of informatio about the reaction when the optical density or relative optica density of the solution is plotted against equivalents of titrant adde (usually expressed as volume of titrant added), but many of thes early investigators did not trouble to plot their results. They wer content to detect the end-point by a large deflection of a galvano meter needle, where the galvanometer reading was a measur of the transmission of the solution. In favourable instance a large deflexion of the needle does occur at the equivalenc point, but for such systems a visual titration will generally suffic anyway. The only satisfactory use of this arrangement is i automatic titrations where a marked change in transmission at th equivalence point can be used to operate a relay to terminate the titration.

Certain other workers plotted the transmission of the solution against equivalents of titrant added and correctly determined the end-point as a break on the curve. However, the end-point is

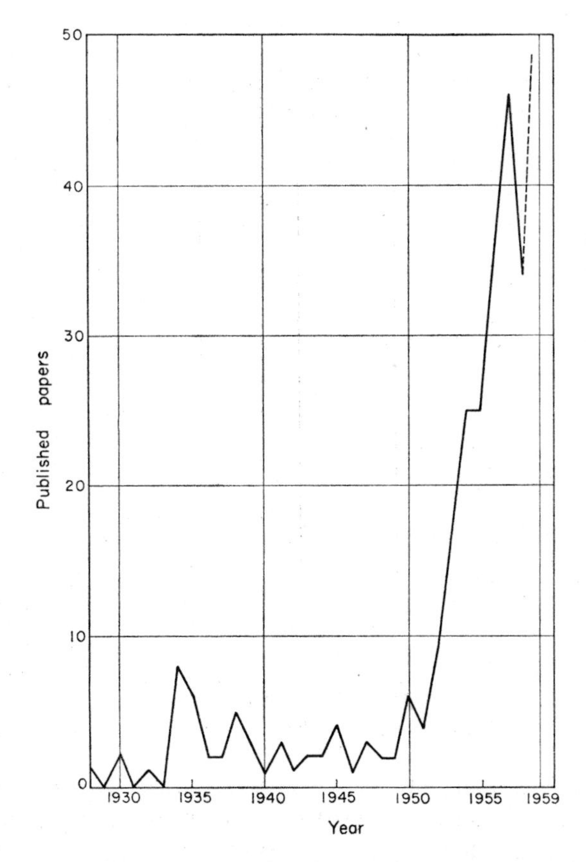

FIG. 1. Distribution of published papers on photometric titration

determined with much greater accuracy by employing optical density instead of transmission as the ordinate (a fact which was overlooked by these investigators) for by the use of optical density readings the end-point occurs at the intersection of straight lines.

Some chemists did, of course, employ the correct type of plot e.g. Müller *et al.*[4] in their investigations on the starch–iodine reaction but photometric titrations did not become popular until commercia spectrophotometers had been installed in most laboratories. Th first use of a spectrophotometer for photometric titrations in whic the titrant is added directly to the titration cell, appears to have beer made in 1949 by Hindeman *et al.*[5] who carried out titrations o neptunium (IV) sulphate with ceric sulphate solution, and of neptunium (VI) chloride with solutions of stannous chloride anc ferrous ions using a Beckman spectrophotometer.

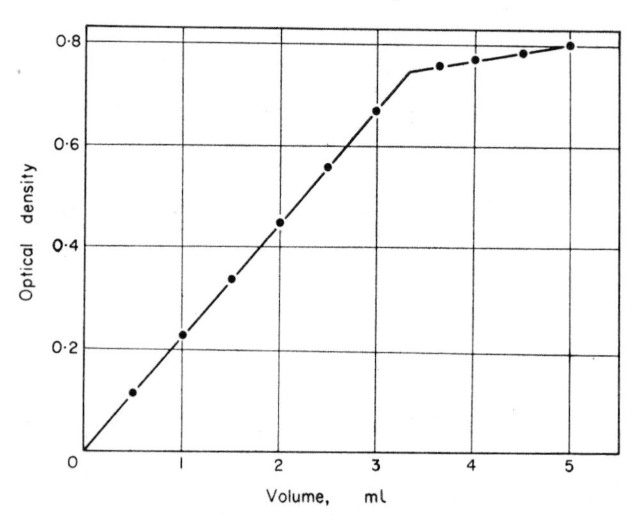

FIG. 2. Titration of about 1·8 mg of iron (II) with approx. 0·01 M cobalt (III) sulphate at 360 mμ
(By courtesy of *Analytical Chemistry*)

About three hundred papers on photometric titrations had appeared in the literature up to the end of 1959 and Fig. 1 shows that the technique has increased greatly in popularity since 1952. Reviews or articles on photometric titrations have been written by Goddu and Hume[6], Underwood[7], Headridge[8], and Musha and Ogawa[9]. Bobtelsky[10] has written a book on *Heterometry* and Zyka[11] a review on heterometric titrations.

Types of titration

1.3 I Self-indicator systems, i.e. titrations without the use of n added indicator. An example of a titration in this class is that of errous ions with cobaltic ions[12] (Fig. 2). Visual titrations on soluions in this class can only be performed when either the species eing titrated or the titrating substance absorbs very strongly in the isible region of the spectrum, e.g. the titration of ferrous ions with ermanganate ions. Almost all photometric titrations performed n the ultra-violet or very near infra-red regions of the spectrum re in this class. So too are titrations to maximum turbidity.

With these titrations the end-point is almost always the interection of straight lines if the reaction is complete at the end-point. A few titrations are exceptions, e.g. the turbidimetric ultra-micro itration of potassium[13].) Obviously these plots are of various types epending on whether or not there is absorption by the initial pecies in the solution, the reaction products and the titrant. hese different types of photometric plots are discussed by Goddu nd Hume[6] and their various shapes are illustrated in Fig. 3 with xamples taken from the literature. The theoretical slopes for plots f this type are easily calculated from Beer's Law if the composiions of the absorbing species present in the solution during the itration are known.

When the reaction is incomplete at the end-point that portion of he plot near the end-point is rounded, e.g. titration of *p*-bromohenol with sodium hydroxide as shown in Fig. 4[6]. However the nd-point is still readily obtained by extrapolating the straight line ortions of the plot until they intersect. This simple method of xtrapolation has been used successfully by many workers, but for he most exact results a mathematical method has been evolved by Grunwald[18] for determining the end-point, when there is curvature n its vicinity. Incompleteness of reaction at the end-point may be aused, for example, by neutralization of very weak acids and ases, oxidation-reduction reactions involving couples with oxidation otentials not greatly differing in magnitude, slight dissociation of a omplex, appreciable solubility of an "insoluble precipitate", and eactions which are slow to come to equilibrium in the vicinity of he end-point.

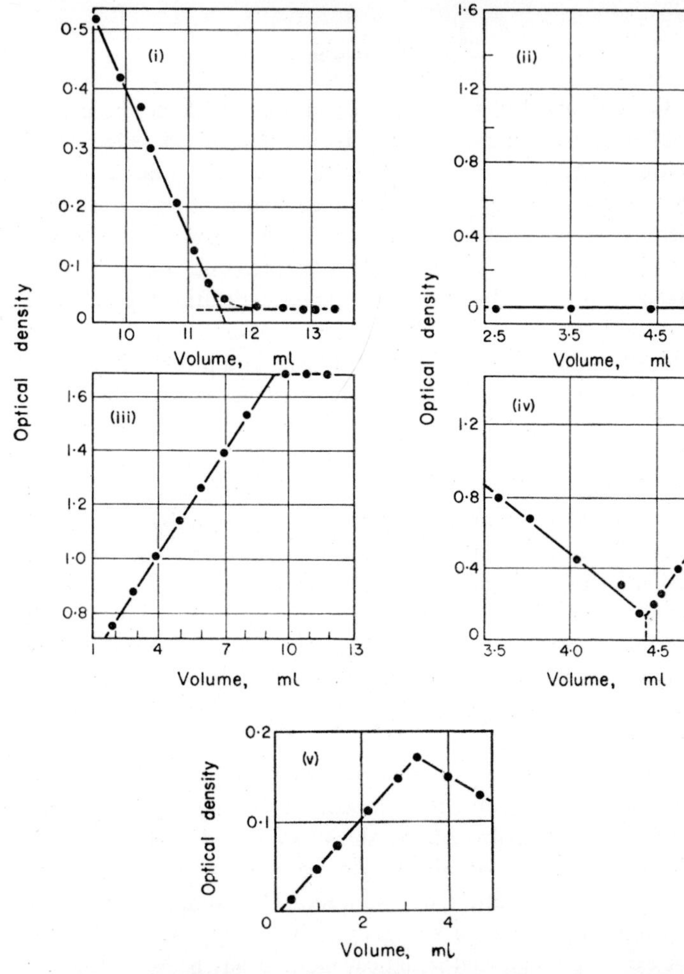

FIG. 3. (i) Titration of about 150 mg of *o*-chloroaniline in glacial acetic acid with 0·1 N acetous perchloric acid at 312 mμ[14]. (ii) Titration of about 5·4 mg of uranium (IV) with approx. 0·01 N ceric sulphate solution at 360 mμ[15]. (iii) Titration of about 120 mg of quinoline in glacial acetic acid with 0·1 N acetous perchloric acid at 350 mμ[14]. (iv) Titration of about 12·8 mg of antimony (III) in 6 N hydrochloric acid with 0·1 N potassium bromate–potassium bromide solution at 326 mμ. (About 8·8 mg of arsenic (III) in the same solution had already been titrated[16].) (By courtesy of *Analytical Chemistry*) (v) Titration of about 10·4 mg of lead as nitrate in 50% (v/v) aqueous alcohol with 0·005 M trisodium citrate[17].

1.4 II Titrations in solutions containing an indicator. With very few exceptions these apply only to acid-base and complexometric titrations. The shapes of the titration curves for the photometric titration of acids and bases with added indicator are discussed in detail in sections 1.11 to 1.15. A study of the literature shows that only a few papers have been published on this type of acid-base titration.

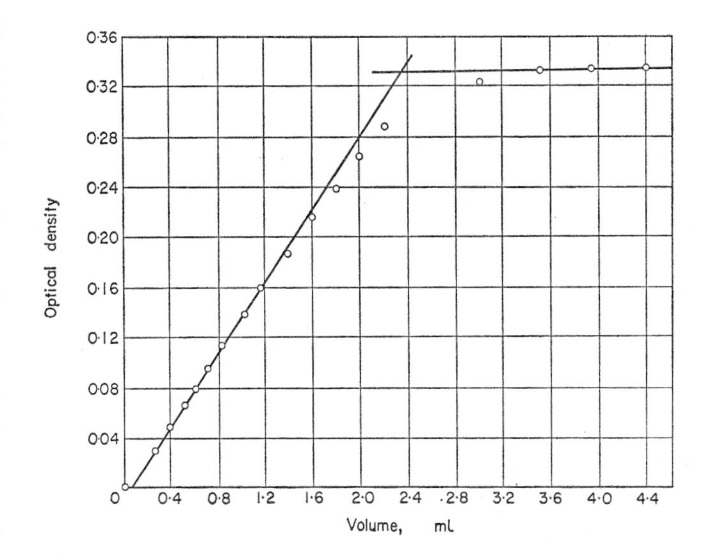

FIG. 4. Titration of about 48 mg of *p*-bromophenol with 0·12 N sodium hydroxide at 325 mμ. (By courtesy of *Analytical Chemistry*)

On the other hand, much published information is available on complexometric titrations in the presence of an indicator. A detailed study of theoretical titration curves for these systems is given in section 1.16. However, since these titrations form a large proportion of all photometric titrations, it is reasonable, at this stage, to consider briefly the shapes of these titration curves. A glance at published titration plots (optical density against volume of titrant added) shows that in many cases the end-point occurs at the intersection of a curve and a straight line and not at the intersection of two straight lines, as is almost always the case with titrations in self-indicator systems. (In this discussion roundness in the vicinity of the end-point is considered to be absent.) A typical example is the titration of zinc with EDTA in the presence of eriochrome black T as indicator[19] (Fig. 5).

This curvature of one of the lines occurs when the metal-indicator complex has a fairly low stability constant, and this is often the case when organic dyes such as murexide and eriochrome black T are employed. If the metal-indicator complex has a high stability constant, curvature of the line does not occur and the end-point is

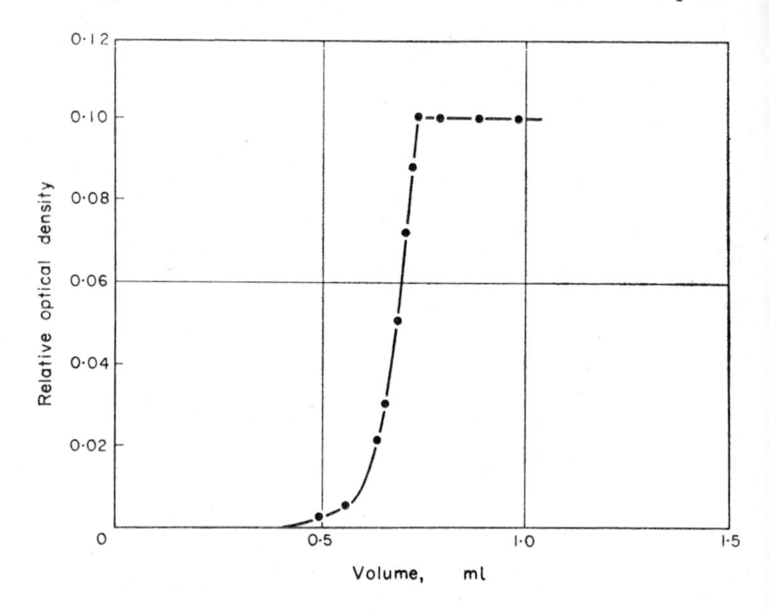

FIG. 5. Titration of about 100 μg of zinc with 0·0025 M EDTA at 665 mμ (indicator: eriochrome black T)

located at the intersection of two straight lines. An example is the titration of iron (III) with EDTA using salicylic acid as indicator[20] (Fig. 6). If the metal-indicator complex in the solution has a concentration lower than that calculated for 100% formation then it is obvious that some dissociation has occurred owing to the rather low stability constant of the complex. This dissociation can be considerably suppressed by adding the indicator in excess of the metal. This decreases the curvature of the line and the plot approaches more closely to the ideal where the end-point is the intersection of two straight lines. However, this can only be done when the free indicator and metal-indicator complexes have low molar extinction coefficients and this is often not so. Most organic metal indicators and their metal complexes have high molar extinction coefficients and can only be used in very low concentrations.

Where there is roundness in the vicinity of the end-point, and this often occurs, it is evident that the most accurate end-point locations will be made in systems for which the titration plot consists of two

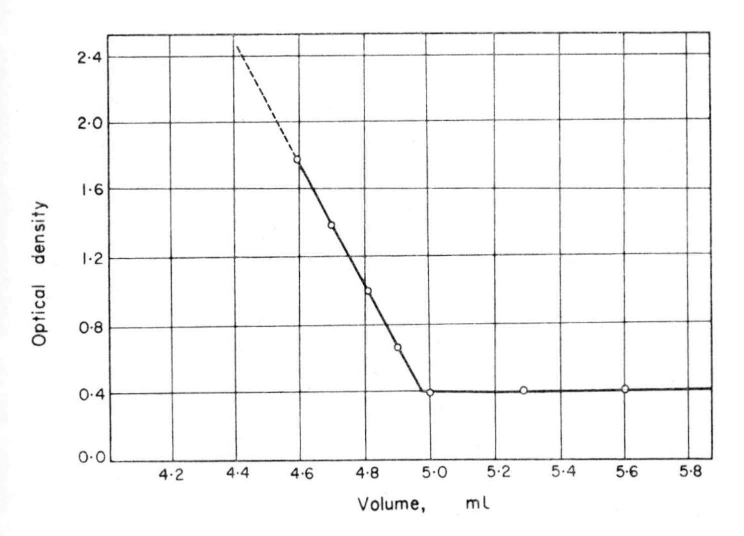

FIG. 6. Titration of about 28 mg of iron (III) with 0·1 M EDTA at 525 mμ (indicator: salicylic acid). (By courtesy of *Analytical Chemistry*)

straight lines extrapolated to intersect at the end-point; but very often these ideal conditions cannot be attained, and then it is necessary to extrapolate the steepest portion of a curve and a straight line, in order to get the best value for the equivalence point.

1.5 Application of photometric titrations. Today, most photometric titrations are carried out for the quantitative analysis of a substance in solution, as will be evident from the later chapters in this monograph. However, this is by no means their only application and they have been used to study the combining properties of a reagent, the species formed by oxidation or reduction, etc. For example, spectrophotometric titrations of aqueous and water–alcohol solutions of cobaltous nitrate with potassium thiocyanate have shown that the species $[Co(NCS)]^{+}$ and $[Co(NCS)_6]^{4-}$ are formed in solution[21]. Also, by spectrophotometric titration of an aqueous solution of pararosaniline hydrochloride with palladous chloride solution, it has been established that the reaction product is $2C_{19}H_{17}N_3HCl{\cdot}3PdCl_2$.[22] In fact, in the field of precipitation titrations a major use of photometric end-point detection is for the elucidation of the compositions of insoluble species. In the opinion of the author, the application of photometric precipitation titrations for quantitative analysis is very limited. For most systems, other more reliable analytical methods are already available.

Sources of error

1.6 Light not monochromatic. When the light is not monochromatic Beer's Law may not hold. With spectrophotometers and dilute solutions, Beer's Law is usually adhered to except when measurements are being made at a very sharp absorption maximum. However, with filter photometers, failures of Beer's Law are much more common because the transmission band for the filter does not always fall completely in a region where the absorption spectrum of the species to be determined shows a broad, flat maximum. Sandell[23] has illustrated the failure of Beer's Law for the determination of the concentration of potassium chromate solution using a blue filter. In cases where the law is not obeyed, the optical density is less than it should be at high concentration and a plot of optical density against concentration will give a curve concave downwards. Workers employing filter photometers for photometric titrations should always bear in mind that Beer's Law may not be obeyed for the particular system which is being investigated.

1.7 Effect of dilution. For self-indicator systems a plot of optical density against volume of titrant added, produces straight lines if there is complete reaction at the equivalence point and if it is assumed that the volume change of the solution throughout the titration is negligible. However, in actual practice the volume change is seldom negligible and straight lines are therefore obtained only if a correction for volume change is made. The optical density readings are usually corrected to the initial volume of the solution by multiplying the optical density readings by the factor, $(V + v)/V$, where V is the initial volume of the solution and v is the volume of titrant added for the particular optical density reading being considered. When this correction for volume change is not applied, the lines are no longer straight but curve down towards the volume axis.

Workers should use their own discretion about whether or not to apply volume change corrections to their particular system. It is obvious that a volume change correction must be applied when the end-point is taken as the intersection of extrapolated straight lines, and when this method of end-point determination is applied, Goddu and Hume[6] have recommended that corrections should be made if the increase in volume exceeds 1%.

The volume change is, of course, small when the titrant is added at a concentration considerably greater than that of the titrand and it is as well to arrange for this when volume change corrections are not to be applied. It is obvious from reading the literature on photometric titrations that most workers have found it unnecessary to apply corrections for volume change, but it should always be borne in mind that failure to take volume change into account may result in an error in end-point location.

1.8 Effect of changes of temperature. The stability constants of complexes are temperature-dependent, and an increase in temperature of a solution containing a complex as the absorbing species may result in a decrease in the optical density of the solution owing to increased dissociation of the complex. During the course of a photometric titration the temperature of the solution is unlikely to be appreciably affected by external temperature changes, but the heat of reaction of the titrand and titrant, and the frictional heat of the stirrer, may cause a rise in temperature with a resulting effect on the optical density of the solution. However, in the vast majority of cases, photometric titrations are performed with very dilute solutions and temperature changes from the former effect are negligible. Conditions can generally be arranged so that frictional heat from the stirrer is also negligible. If an increase in temperature during the titration of more concentrated solutions has an effect on the optical density readings then the titration can be carried out in a thermostatically controlled vessel, but such refinements are seldom necessary.

1.9 Effect of stray light. Every effort should be made to get the titration cell as light-proof from stray light as possible. Stray light causes the optical density readings to be lower than they would be in its absence, and this effect gets worse as the optical density of the solution increases. With spectrophotometers the titration assembly should be built in such a way that errors due to stray light are negligible for optical density readings $\leqslant 1$. Suitable arrangements will be described in the next chapter. It is, of course, an easy matter to check that the stray light error is negligible for a titration assembly by choosing as titrant a solution of an absorbing species known to obey Beer's Law, and by adding increments of this titrant to distilled water in the cell until the optical density of the solution exceeds 1. A plot of optical density readings (corrected for volume change) against volume of titrant added, should produce a straight line at least as far as optical density equal to 1.

Theoretical titration curves

1.10 Acid base titrations: self-indicator systems. The theoretical shapes of photometric titration curves for the titration of a weak acid in aqueous solution by a strong base or vice versa are readily determined for self-indicator systems[24].

For a system where the undissociated acid is colourless and the anion, formed in the titration, coloured, the appropriate equation for relating the fraction of coloured anion to the fraction of acid titrated is obtained as follows.

Let the initial concentration of acid (HA) be S.

Let the amount of alkali (NaOH) added be equivalent to a concentration, X.

Assume no volume change during the titration.

Then

$$X = [\mathrm{Na}^+] \text{ and } S = [\mathrm{HA}] + [\mathrm{A}^-]$$

$$[\mathrm{A}^-] = [\mathrm{Na}^+] + [\mathrm{H}^+] - [\mathrm{OH}^-]$$

$$= X + K_{\mathrm{A}} \frac{[\mathrm{HA}]}{[\mathrm{A}^-]} - \frac{K_{\mathrm{W}}}{K_{\mathrm{A}}} \frac{[\mathrm{A}^-]}{[\mathrm{HA}]}$$

$$= X + K_{\mathrm{A}} \frac{(S - [\mathrm{A}^-])}{[\mathrm{A}^-]} - \frac{K_{\mathrm{W}}}{K_{\mathrm{A}}} \frac{[\mathrm{A}^-]}{(S - [\mathrm{A}^-])}$$

Therefore $\frac{X}{S}$ = fraction of acid titrated

$$= y - \frac{K_A}{S}\frac{1-y}{y} + \frac{K_W}{K_A.S}\frac{y}{1-y} \quad (1)$$

where $y = \frac{[A^-]}{S}$ = fraction of coloured anion produced.

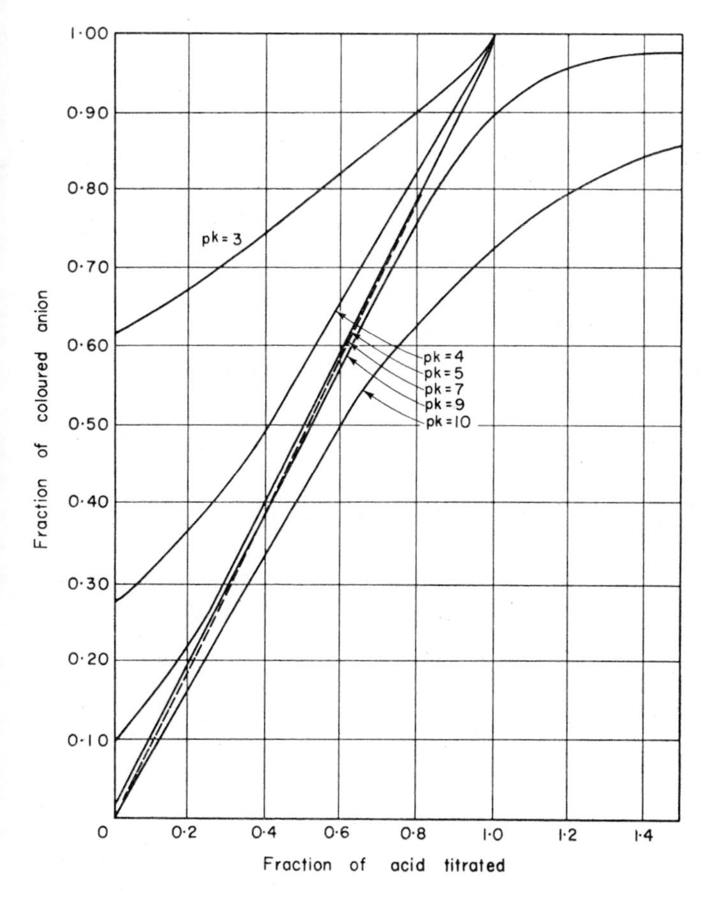

FIG. 7. Theoretical photometric titration curves for acids of various K's at concentration = 10^{-3} M. (By courtesy of *Analytical Chemistry*)

Figure 7 shows the plots obtained by Goddu and Hume[24] at various pK_A values for an initial acid concentration of 10^{-3} M using equation

(1). If Beer's Law is obeyed similar plots will be obtained for a graph of optical density against volume of titrant added.

Goddu and Hume[24] concluded from a study of plots obtained at various pK_A values for different initial acid concentrations, that a weak acid of the type just considered could generally be titrated satisfactorily with photometric end-point detection provided that the acid concentration was 10^{-5} M or above, and that the product of dissociation constant and concentration was equal to or greater than 10^{-12}.

Acid-base titrations: indicator added

1.11 Theoretical titration curves for these systems may also be calculated. The equation for a plot of fraction of indicator in the basic form against fraction of a weak acid titrated by a strong base, is derived below.

The pertinent equilibrium is

$$A^- + HI^+ \rightleftharpoons HA + I$$

where HA and A^- are the weak acid and conjugate base respectively, and HI^+ and I, the acidic and basic forms of the indicator respectively.

Then

$$K = \frac{[HA]\,[I]}{[A^-]\,[HI^+]} = \frac{K_I}{K_A}$$

where $K_I = [H^+]\,[I]/[HI^+]$, the dissociation constant of the acidic form of the indicator, and $K_A = [H^+]\,[A^-]/[HA]$, the dissociation constant of the acid. If the initial concentration of acid in the system is S and if the amount of alkali added is equivalent to a concentration, X, then

$$K = \frac{[I]}{[IH^+]} \cdot \frac{(S-X)}{X} \tag{2}$$

if we assume that the concentration of the free base is negligible up to the end-point.

Rearranging

$$K\frac{[IH^+]}{[I]} = \frac{S}{X} - 1$$

therefore

$$K\left(\frac{[IH^+] + [I]}{[I]}\right) = \frac{S}{X} - 1 + K$$

Hence
$$K = \left(\frac{S}{X} - 1 + K\right) F$$

where F is the fraction of indicator in the basic form and S/X is the reciprocal of the fraction of acid titrated. A plot of F against X/S is given in Fig. 8 as taken from the paper by Higuchi *et al.*[25] for a system where $K = 0{\cdot}1$.

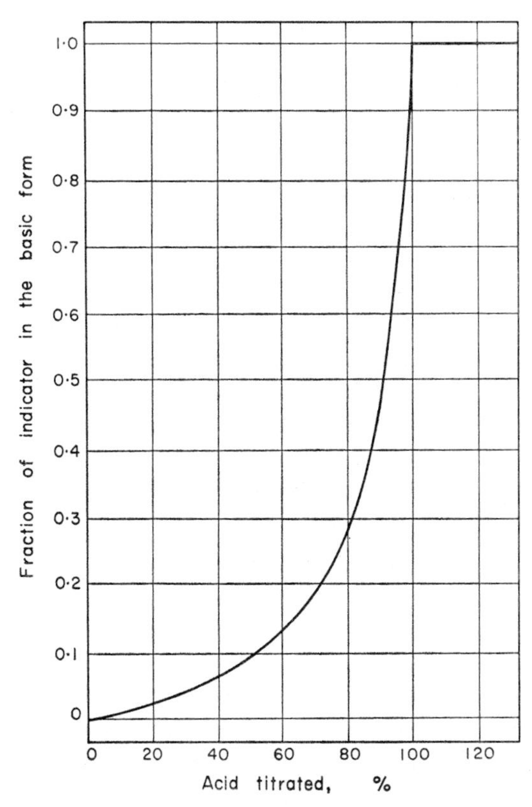

FIG. 8. Idealized plot of indicator absorbance during titration of weak acid with strong base where $K = 0{\cdot}1$. (By courtesy of *Analytical Chemistry*)

If Beer's Law holds and the basic form of the dye is coloured while the acidic form is colourless, then an identical plot of optical density against volume of base added will be obtained for a system where there is a negligible increase in volume during the titration.

1.12 By rearranging equation (2), Higuchi *et al.*[25] obtained

$$XK\frac{[IH^+]}{[I]} = S - X \tag{3}$$

Very near to the end-point, X is nearly equal to S and it is possible to write

$$SK\frac{[IH^+]}{[I]} = S - X \tag{4}$$

A plot of values of $[IH^+]/[I]$, obtained just before the end-point, against X therefore produces a straight line whose intercept on the X axis is equal to S, the amount of base stoichiometrically required to neutralize the weak acid. This type of plot gives excellent results for the end-point when $K \leqslant 0{\cdot}01$.

1.13 Yet another variation of equation (2) is

$$\frac{1}{X} = \frac{1}{S} + \frac{K}{S}\frac{[IH^+]}{[I]} \tag{5}$$

If $[IH^+]/[I]$ is now plotted against $1/X$, a straight line with intercept on the $1/X$ axis at $1/S$ will result, $1/S$ being the reciprocal of the stoichiometrically required amount of base.

This equation holds over the entire titration range and its application is particularly useful when K values are greater than $0{\cdot}05$.

$[IH^+]/[I]$ values are, of course, calculated from the optical density readings during the titration since

$$\frac{[IH^+]}{[I]} = \frac{A_B - A}{A}$$

where A_B is the optical density of the pure basic form of the indicator and A is the optical density during the course of the titration, if the basic form absorbs and the acidic form does not.

Similar equations hold for the titration of weak bases with strong acids but here $[I]/[IH^+]$ is now plotted as the ordinate instead of $[IH^+]/[I]$.

1.14 Rehm and Higuchi[26] have also derived an equation which can be applied to the titration of extremely weak bases in aqueous or glacial acetic acid solution in the presence of an even weaker base as indicator. In these systems the indicator colour change occurs almost entirely after the base has been titrated. The necessary equilibrium reaction for aqueous solutions is therefore

$$H_2O + IH^+ \rightleftharpoons H_3O^+ + I$$

therefore $$K_I = \frac{[I]\,[H_3O^+]}{[IH^+]} \quad \text{or} \quad [H_3O^+] = K_I \frac{[IH^+]}{[I]} \qquad (6)$$

where K_I is the dissociation constant of the acidic form of the indicator. If P g-equiv. is the amount of monobasic acid required to convert the base being titrated, stoichiometrically to its conjugate acid and Z g-equiv. is the total amount of acid added, then

$$Z - P = K_I \frac{[IH^+]}{[I]} \cdot V$$

where V is the total volume of solution in the titration vessel. Thus, a plot of $[IH^+]/[I]$ against Z will yield a straight line with an intercept on the Z axis corresponding to P.

1.15 For all the equations derived in this section, no account was taken of the possible solvolysis of the salt formed during the titration. Higuchi has revealed that, for small samples, deviations from linearity may occur on plots based on equations (5) and (6) when solvolysis of the salt is not negligible. Modifications of these equations have therefore been made to take this solvolysis into account[27, 28].

1.16 Complexometric titrations: indicator added. Colour change curves, i.e. percentage colour change plotted against equivalents of titrant added have been theoretically derived by a number of workers for the titration of metal ions with EDTA using indicators[29, 30, 31, 32]. Certain of these curves were derived for highly specific systems. Schwarzenbach[31], for example, has considered the systems, magnesium + eriochrome black T + EDTA, calcium + murexide + EDTA and calcium + metalphthalein + EDTA. A less extensive treatment of the photometric titrations of EDTA with cupric sulphate using murexide as indicator and of magnesium sulphate with EDTA using eriochrome black T, has also been made by Ringbom and Vänninen[32].

However, Reilley and Schmid[33] have recently derived equations that can be applied to any system and, since colour change curves have great bearing on photometric titrations, their equations are reproduced below.

For the system in question, it is necessary first of all to construct a pM–pH diagram containing information relating to the initial pM of the solution (the A line), the pM when the solution is 100% overtitrated (the C line), and the pM value at which the indicator is present 50% in the free dye form and 50% in the metal-indicator complex form (the B line). Figure 9 is the pM–pH diagram for the system magnesium ion–EDTA–eriochrome black T. The equation for line A is

$$pM_A = -\log C_M \quad (1)$$

where C_M is the initial concentration of the free metal ion. Equation (1) is valid only when no precipitating or complexing agents are

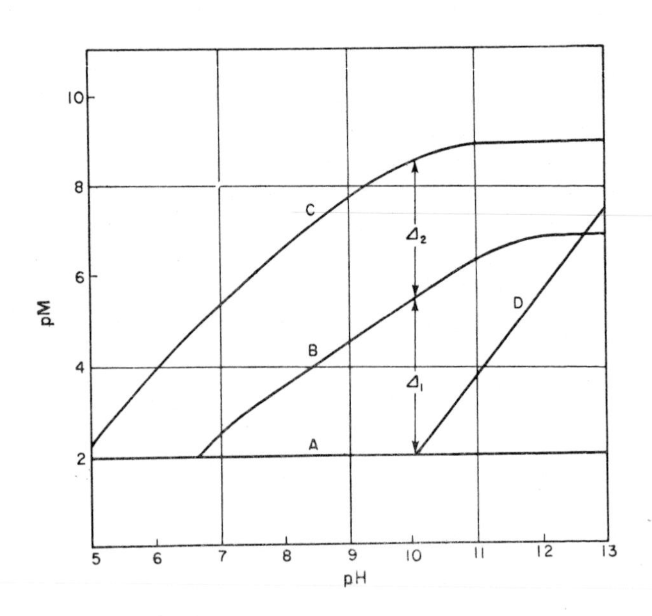

FIG. 9. Titration of magnesium with EDTA using eriochrome black T as indicator. (By courtesy of *Analytical Chemistry*)

present. (In Fig. 9 the initial concentration of magnesium ions falls above pH 10·2 because of the precipitation of magnesium hydroxide. This is shown by line D.) The equation for line B is

$$pM_B = \log K_{MIn} - \log \alpha_{In} = \log K'_{MIn} \quad (2)$$

for a 1 : 1 metal-indicator complex.

K'_{MIn} is the effective stability constant of the metal-indicator complex. $K'_{MIn} = K_{MIn}/\alpha_{In}$, where K_{MIn} is the true stability constant and

$$\alpha_{In} = 1 + \frac{[H^+]}{k_n} + \frac{[H^+]^2}{k_n k_{n-1}} + \ldots\ldots + \frac{[H^+]^n}{\pi_n k_n} \qquad (3)$$

where k_n is the nth acidity constant of the indicator. The equation for line C is

$$pM_C = \log K_{MY} - \log \alpha_Y = \log K'_{MY} \qquad (4)$$

where K'_{MY} is the effective stability constant of the metal-titrant complex. $K'_{MY} = K_{MY}/\alpha_Y$, where K_{MY} is the true stability constant and

$$\alpha_Y = 1 + \frac{[H^+]}{l_n} + \frac{[H^+]^2}{l_n l_{n-1}} + \ldots\ldots + \frac{[H^+]^n}{\pi_n l_n} \qquad (5)$$

where l_n is the nth acidity constant of the titrant.

For a particular pH, the distance apart of the lines A and C and the position of the line B between the lines A and C have a great bearing on the sharpness of the end-point.

A measure of the tightness of the metal-indicator complex is given by Δ_1, which is the distance between the lines A and B. A measure of the extent to which the titrant displaces the indicator from the metal-indicator complex is given by Δ_2, which is the distance between the lines B and C. (In Fig. 9, Δ_1 and Δ_2 are indicated for pH 10.)

Now clearly

$$\Delta_1 = pM_B - pM_A = \log K'_{MIn} + \log C_M$$
$$= \log K_{MIn} - \alpha_{MIn} + \log C_M \qquad (6)$$
$$\text{and } \Delta_2 = pM_C - pM_B = \log K'_{MY} - \log K'_{MIn}$$
$$= \log K_{MY} - \log K_{MIn} - \log \alpha_Y + \log \alpha_{In} \qquad (7)$$

In order to relate end-point sharpness to the end-point indices, Δ_1 and Δ_2, use is made of equation (8) which was derived by Fortuin *et al.*[29] and later by Flaschka *et al.*[30] for the titration curve (percentage colour change against equivalents of titrant added) of a direct complexometric titration using a metallochromic indicator.

$$A = 1 - \frac{(1-y)}{y} \cdot \frac{1}{C_M K'_{MIn}} + \frac{y}{(1-y)} \frac{K'_{MIn}}{K'_{MY}} - \frac{[MIn]}{C_M}$$
$$- \frac{K'_{MIn}(C_{In} - [MIn])}{K'_{MY} C_M} - \frac{1}{C_M K'_{MY}} \qquad (8)$$

where A = ratio of titrant to titrand

y = fractional colour change (fraction of the free indicator)

C_{M} = total metal ion concentration (titrated + untitrated)

C_{In} = total indicator concentration

[MIn] = concentration of the metal-indicator complex

K'_{MY} = effective stability constant of the metal-titrant complex

K'_{MIn} = effective stability constant of the metal-indicator complex

In terms of end-point indices the equation is

$$A = 1 - \left(\frac{1-y}{y}\right)\frac{1}{10^{\Delta_1}} + \left(\frac{y}{1-y}\right)\frac{1}{10^{\Delta_2}} - \frac{1}{C_{\mathrm{M}}10^{\Delta_2}}\left(10^{\Delta_2}[\mathrm{MIn}] + C_{\mathrm{In}} - [\mathrm{MIn}]\right) - \frac{1}{10^{\Delta_1+\Delta_2}} \quad (9)$$

Because $10^{\Delta_1+\Delta_2}$ has to be at least 10^4 to 10^5 to obtain a usable end-point break even for photometric titration, the last term can be neglected. Furthermore in the fourth term, [MIn] can be neglected compared with 10^{Δ_2}[MIn]. Thus the equation simplifies to

$$A = 1 - \left(\frac{1-y}{y}\right)\frac{1}{10^{\Delta_1}} + \left(\frac{y}{1-y}\right)\frac{1}{10^{\Delta_2}} - \frac{C_{\mathrm{In}}}{C_{\mathrm{M}}10^{\Delta_2}}\left(1 + 10^{\Delta_2}(1-y)\right) \quad (10)$$

The colour change therefore depends only on Δ_1, Δ_2 and the ratio $C_{\mathrm{In}}/C_{\mathrm{M}}$. If the ratio of the concentration of indicator to the ion being titrated is 10^{-4} or less, the last term of equation (10) can be neglected. Under these conditions then the only parameters which govern the colour change are Δ_1 and Δ_2

and
$$A = 1 - \left(\frac{1-y}{y}\right)\frac{1}{10^{\Delta_1}} + \left(\frac{y}{1-y}\right)\frac{1}{10^{\Delta_2}} \quad (11)$$

By using equation (11) and various combinations of Δ_1 and Δ_2, Fig. 10 was constructed. The shapes of these titration curves are essentially independent of indicator concentration provided that $C_{\mathrm{In}}/C_{\mathrm{M}} \leqslant 10^{-4}$. It can be seen from the figure that photometric titrations on such systems are unlikely to lead to results more acceptable than those obtained by visual titrations, for two reasons.

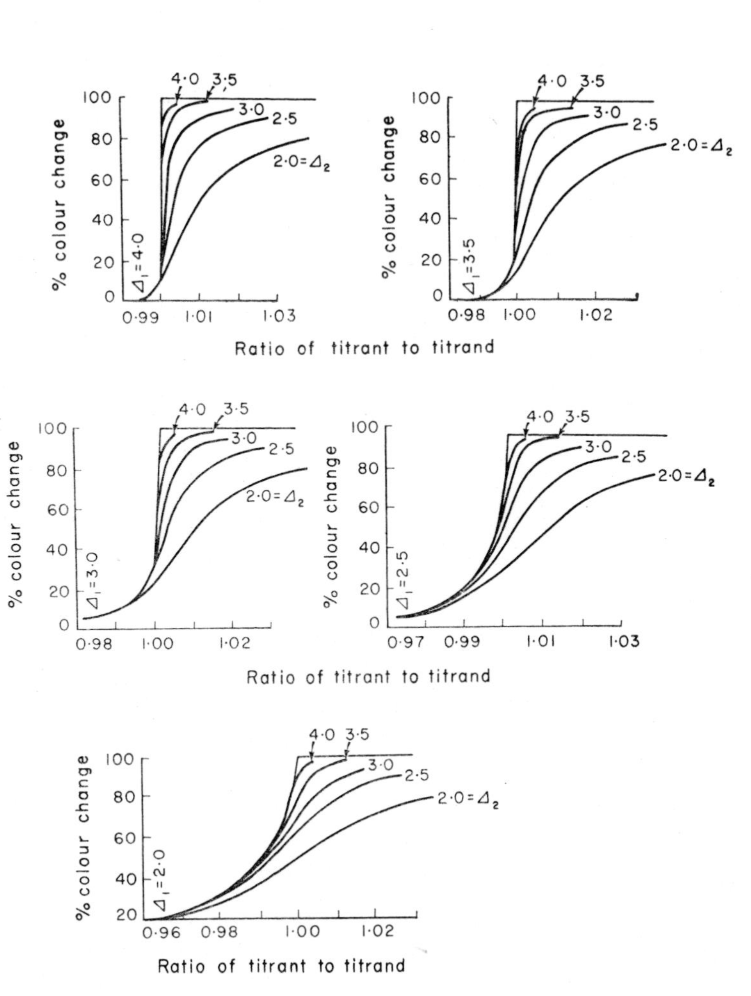

FIG. 10. Colour change curves for various end-point indices (By courtesy of *Analytical Chemistry*)

Firstly, when extrapolation of the appropriate lines on a plot gives the true equivalence point, then a visual titration will be satisfactory anyway; and secondly, when a satisfactory visual titration is impossible, then the usual method of extrapolation will yield apparent end-points considerably greater than the true equivalence points.

It should, however, be remembered that, in actual practice, there are few systems, for which photometric titration might be considered, where C_{In}/C_M is, in fact, $\leqslant 10^{-4}$. In most cases, the effect of indicator concentration must be taken into account.

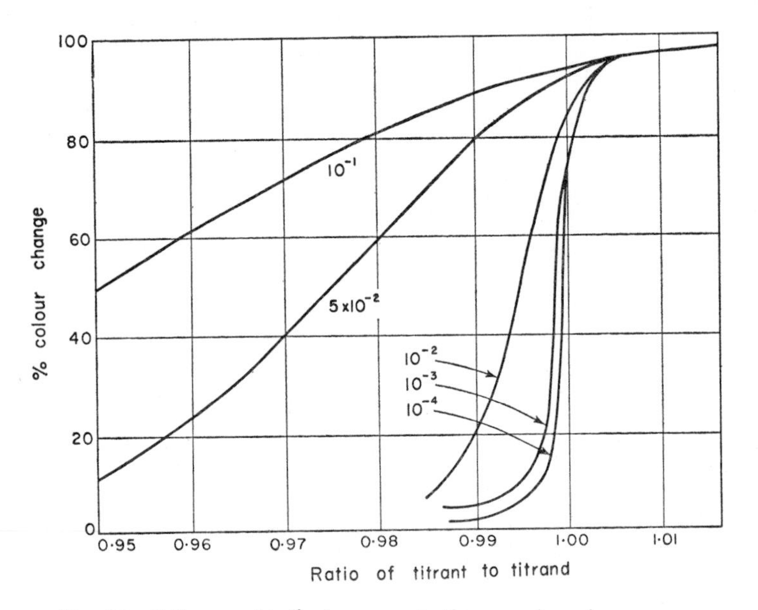

FIG. 11. Influence of indicator concentration on colour change curve. The figures on the curves are C_{In}/C_M values. (By courtesy of *Analytical Chemistry*)

Where $C_{In} > 10^{-4}C_M$, the last term in equation (10) cannot be neglected. However, unless $\Delta_2 > 2$ all accurate end-point determinations are impossible even with the help of a spectrophotometer (see Fig. 10) and therefore the last term of equation (10) simplifies to $(y - 1)C_{In}/C_M$. Figure 11 illustrates the effect of indicator concentration for a system where $\Delta_1 = \Delta_2 = 3{\cdot}5$.

Identical curves will be obtained for plots of optical density against volume of titrant added for suitable systems, i.e. where the instrument is set to measure the absorption of the free indicator at a wavelength where there is no absorption from the metal-indicator complex.

As can be seen from Fig. 11, it is in these cases where $C_{In} > 10^{-2}C_M$ that photometric titration is almost essential if any accuracy is to be attained in end-point detection. Even where $C_{In} = 10^{-1}C_M$ a photometric titration will give a reasonable value for the end-point, although by the method of extrapolation this is likely to be about 0·5% low. The indicator concentration may often have to exceed 10^{-5} M if a reasonable colour intensity is to be detected and with low concentrations of metal ions, say $\leqslant 10^{-3}$ M, C_{In}/C_M will then be $\geqslant 10^{-2}$. These are, in fact, the systems to which photometric end-point detection can be so advantageously applied.

CHAPTER 2

APPARATUS

Commercial instruments

2.1 A few different types of photometric titrators are now manufactured and, if photometric titration is to be used as a routine method, one of these instruments specially designed for this purpose could well be employed. These commercial instruments are discussed in the following paragraphs.

2.2 The EEL Titrator (Evans Electroselenium Limited, Halstead, Essex, England). This is a manual instrument of robust but simple construction. Figure 12 is a photograph of the instrument set up for a titration. It consists essentially of two parts. The first is the unit which contains the light source, a position for the titration cell, a holder for a light filter, a barrier layer photocell, a motor for a magnetic stirrer, and a support for the burette. Two cells are supplied with the instrument, one of 4 ml capacity and the other of 50 ml capacity. Light from the lamp passes through the sample solution and a filter on to the photocell. The optical system is so arranged that the instrument is unaffected by external illumination. The second part is a galvanometer unit which records the current generated by the photocell. The spot light of the galvanometer needle moves over a scale marked in units of both transmission and optical density. During the course of the titration the relative optical density readings are recorded and the end-point is obtained from a plot of optical density against volume of titrant added.

2.3 The Quére Titrator (obtained in Britain from H. Tinsley & Co. Ltd., London). This versatile instrument may be adapted to record photometric titration curves. For photometric titrations a special unit containing a lamp, filters, photocell and motor for a magnetic stirrer, is attached to the basic unit. This consists of a movable table which, during the titration, passes under a ball-point stylus whose movement depends on the relative optical density of the solution. A sheet of graph paper, of which the ordinate is

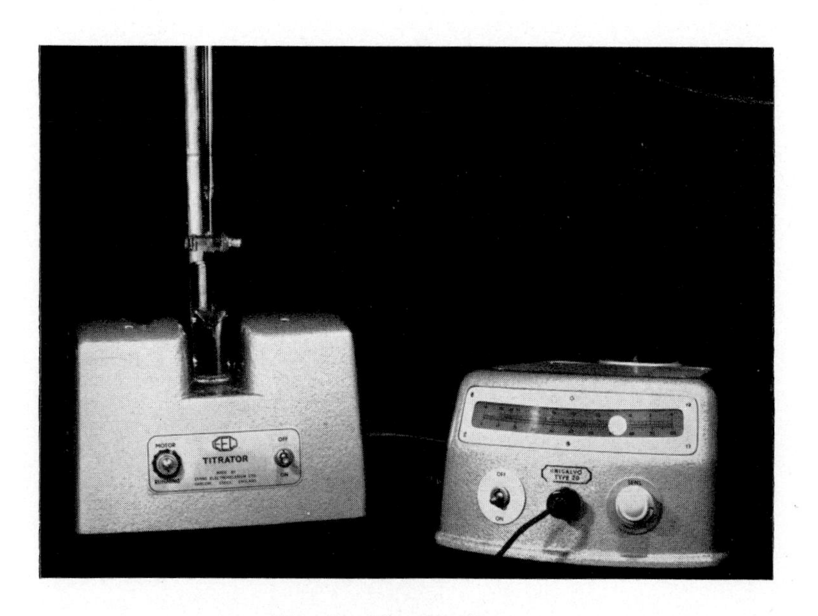

FIG. 12. The EEL Titrator

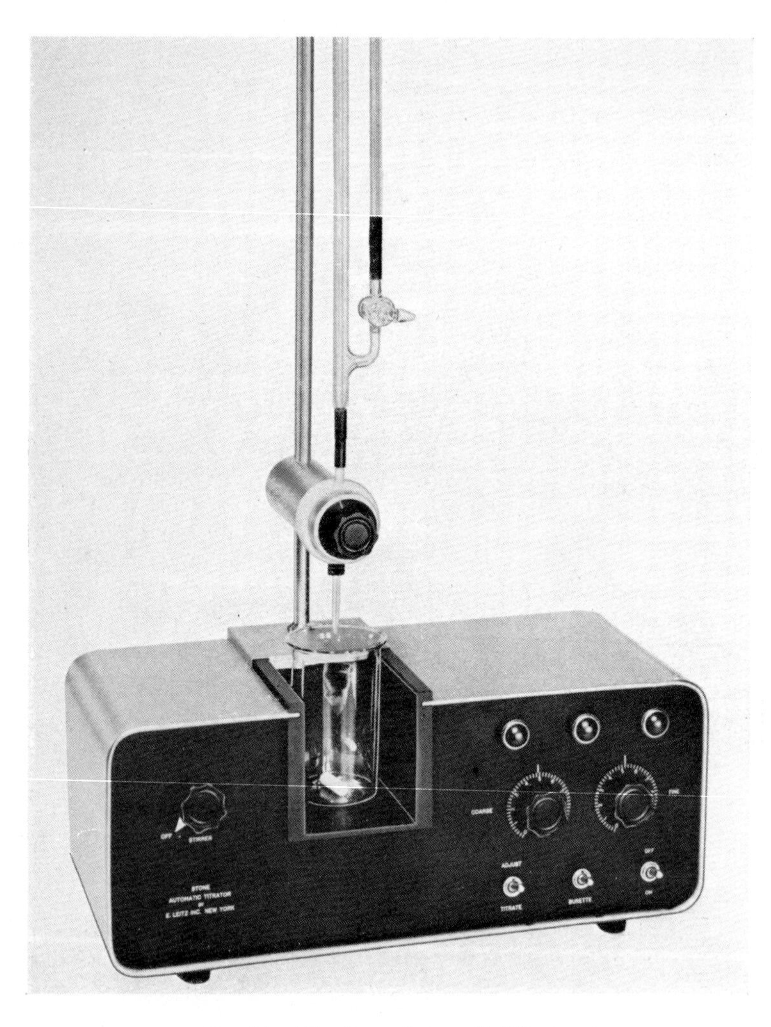

FIG. 14. The Stone Automatic Titrator

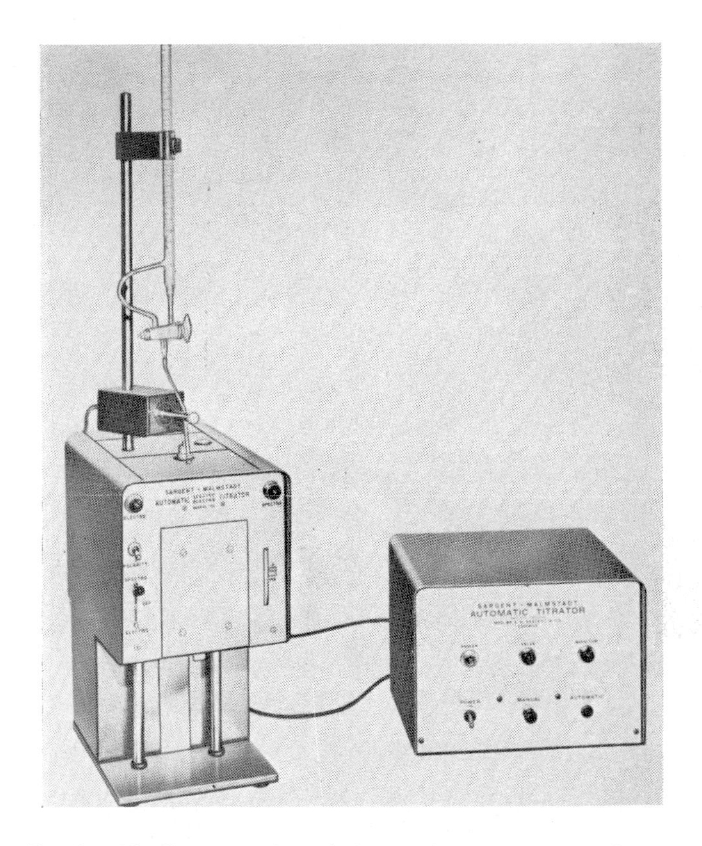

FIG. 15. The Sargent–Malmstadt Automatic Spectro-Electro Titrator

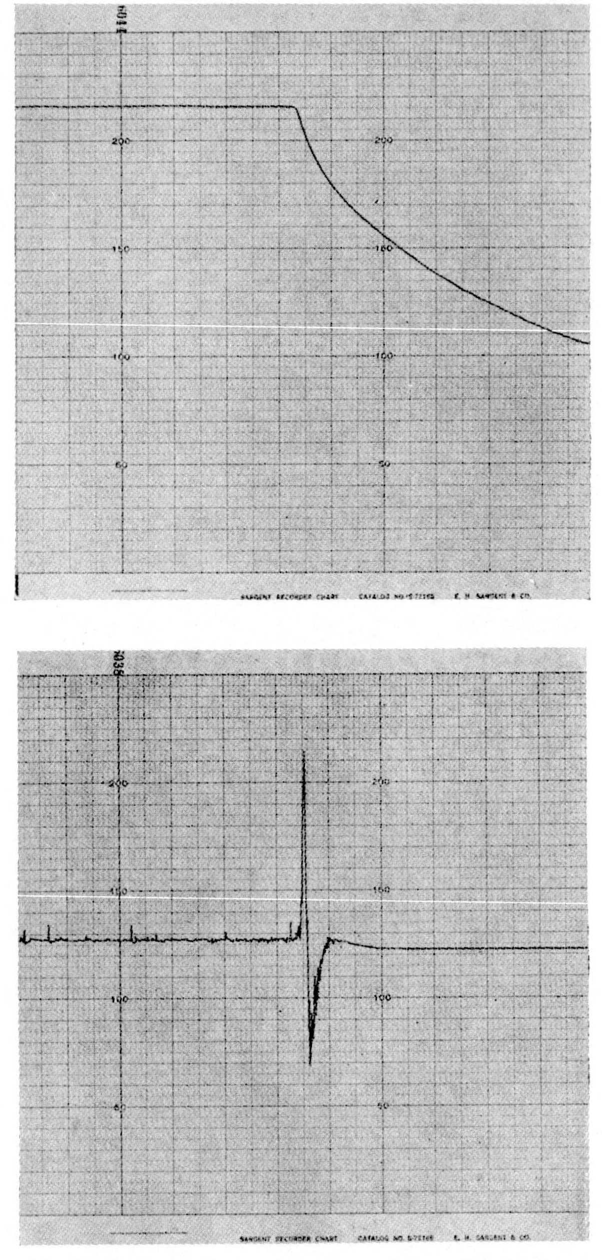

FIG. 16. Basic photocell response curve and second derivative signal obtained from the titration of iron (II) with 0·1 N permanganate at 525 mμ

relative optical density and the abscissa, volume of titrant added, is attached to the table. The movable table rests on a box containing all the necessary electronic circuits for the operation of the instrument. The titrant is added from a syringe whose plunger is geared to the movement of the table. The rate of advance of the table, and hence the rate of addition of titrant, is automatically reduced when the rate of change of the gradient of the curve increases. A typical photometric titration curve obtained with the Quére Titrator is shown in Fig. 13.

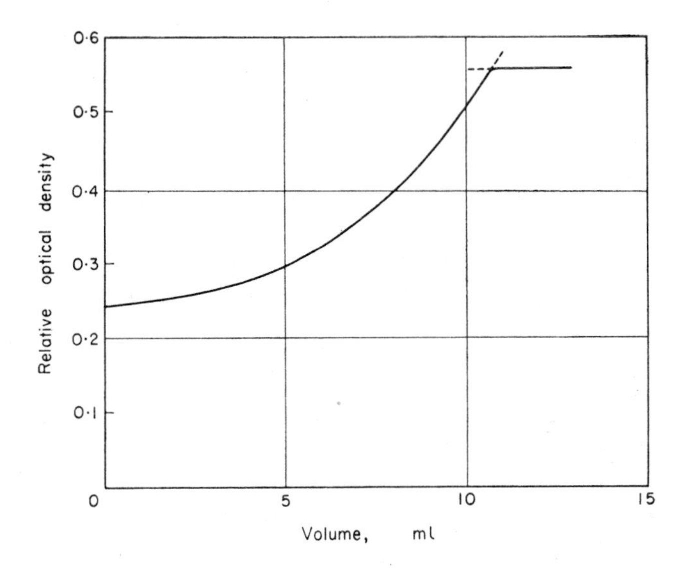

FIG. 13. A curve obtained with the Quére Titrator for the titration of calcium in blood serum with standard EDTA solution using calcon as indicator

The titrator may, of course, also be employed to record potentiometric, conductometric and polarized-electrode titration curves. It can also be adapted for the photoelectric recording of electropherograms and chromatograms.

2.4 The CENCO Titrator (Central Scientific Co., Chicago). This instrument was developed by Thorburn *et al.*[34] and the manufacturers state that it consists of a colour-matic end-point detector and volumatic syringe. It is, in fact, an automatic photometric titrator. With this instrument the end-point is not located from a plot of optical density against volume of titrant added, but the delivery of titrant is automatically stopped by the operation of a relay when the transmission of the solution reaches a set value. If the transmission of the solution increases or decreases after the equivalence point, the controls are set so that the titration is terminated at a high or low transmission value respectively. Obviously the delivery of titrant is only terminated at the true equivalence point when there is a sharp change in transmission at this point. The instrument is therefore most suitable for automatic titrations in systems with good visual end-points.

However, it is not so suitable for titrations in which there is a gradual change in colour in the vicinity of, or after, the equivalence point. Admittedly the instrument can be used to terminate a titration at a given transmission value which, with titrations of the same type, will usually be obtained when identical volumes of titrant have been added beyond the equivalence point. This method of titration is described by Thorburn and co-workers[34]. In some systems of this type the instrument will produce good results, but for titrations in which there is only a very gradual change in transmission after the equivalence point, an appreciable error may arise from the dilution effect.

The titrant is added from a syringe, the movement of the plunger being controlled by a motor. The volume of titrant added is obtained from a number shown on a mechanical counter. The counter is operated from the motor and 288 counts are recorded for the addition of every 1 ml of titrant. Titrations are carried out in a 250 ml beaker using a magnetic stirrer. The optical system is simple, the light transmitted by the solution passing through a filter on to a cadmium sulphide cell which acts as a detector.

2.5 The Stone Automatic Titrator (E. Leitz, Inc., New York). This is a compact instrument, shown in Fig. 14. A beam of light from the light source passes through the solution which is being titrated and is then split into two beams which fall upon a pair of photocells. One of the light beams passes through a filter. The output of the photocell is adjusted by means of a coarse and fine control to establish balance as shown by an indicator light. The colour change at the end-point of the titration unbalances the circuit, actuates a solenoid valve on the burette and instantly cuts off the supply of titrant. Titrations may be carried out in beakers of 30 to 600 ml capacity. Mixing is done with a magnetic stirrer. An adjustable time-delay mechanism is incorporated in the instrument to prevent the premature cut-off of titrant, which, because of slow stirring or reaction, could result from the appearance, before the end-point, of the substance whose colour is to be used to unbalance the circuit at the true end-point.

The instrument gives excellent results when there is a sharp colour change at the end-point. Although it could certainly be used in many systems where there is a gradual colour change in the vicinity of, or after, the end-point, the results are unlikely to be so reliable. In this respect the instrument resembles the CENCO Titrator.

2.6 Sargent-Malmstadt Automatic Spectro-Electro Titrator (E. H. Sargent & Co., Chicago). This is a dual purpose instrument designed to perform both potentiometric and photometric titrations automatically[35]. This instrument has been developed mainly as a result of the work of Malmstadt and co-workers. That part of the instrument used for potentiometric titrations was developed from the Sargent–Malmstadt Automatic Potentiometric Titrator, a commercial instrument which has been available for some years. That section of the instrument used in automatic photometric titrations is a development of earlier instruments described by Malmstadt *et al.*[36, 37]

The instrument consists of two units as shown in Fig. 15. The first holds a lamp, a platform support for the titration cell, a set of filters, a photocell, a motor-driven stirring rod, and a burette fitted with a solenoid shut-off valve. Beakers of 30–600 ml capacity are used as titration cells. The filters are of the interference type, capable of selecting a narrow band of wavelength in the order of 10–20 mμ band width. Six filters are supplied. These in their primary or higher order transmission bands cover the wavelength range of 370–650 mμ. Two photocells are provided. A barrier-layer cell is used over most of the visible region of the spectrum, but is not sufficiently sensitive in the violet and near ultra-violet regions where it is replaced by a cadmium sulphide photo-resistive cell.

The second unit is the control unit which processes the signal from the photocell and operates the solenoid shut-off valve of the burette.

If the plot of photocell response against volume of titrant added shows a break at the equivalence point, then the titration can be terminated by using the second derivative signal to operate the solenoid shut-off valve of the burette. For the titration of ferrous ions with permanganate, photocell response and second derivative signal curves are as shown in Fig. 16. The flow of titrant is stopped at that moment when the second derivative signal falls from its maximum to its minimum value. This type of second derivative signal curve results when the photocell response curve exhibits a point of inflection. When the point of inflection occurs at the end-point then the second derivative signal stops the titration at that point. First, second and third derivative curves have been discussed in a paper by Malmstadt and Roberts[36].

This titrator has certain distinct advantages when compared with the Stone and CENCO Automatic Titrators, for it can be employed to give good results in all systems for which there is a point of inflection on the photocell response curve coincident with the end-point.

The photocell response is approximately directly proportional to the transmission of the solution and if the plot of optical density against volume of titrant added has a break at the end-point, then the plot of transmission against volume of titrant added does likewise. Hence the Sargent–Malmstadt Titrator should indicate the true end-point, provided that the photocell response curve consists of two lines with an abrupt change of gradient at the end-point. However, where there is extensive roundness in the vicinity of the end-point on this curve, then the point of inflection may be well removed from the end-point and inaccurate results will be obtained.

2.7 In considering the merits of the various instruments that have just been described, the following points are worthy of mention. The CENCO and Stone Titrators give their most reliable results when there is a sharp colour change at the end-point. The Sargent–Malmstadt Titrator will function satisfactorily when there is, at the end-point, a sharp change in gradient of the curve of transmission, and also optical density plotted against volume of titrant added. However, for the location of "difficult" end-points where, for example, there may be extensive roundness in the vicinity of the end-point, then there is no doubt that the most accurate location of the end-point is made after studying the actual plot of optical density against volume of titrant added, and these plots are only obtained with the EEL and Quére Titrators.

2.8 The Leco ASD-1 Automatic Sulphur Titrator. A description of this instrument completes the section on commercial instruments. The Leco Titrator[38] is a specialized instrument devised for the determination of sulphur in steel, limestone, oils and rubber by combustion of the sulphur to sulphur dioxide. The sulphur dioxide from the combustion unit passes into the titration cell which contains acidified potassium iodide solution, starch indicator and iodine which has itself been produced by the addition of standard iodate solution from a burette fitted with a solenoid valve. When sufficient sulphur dioxide has passed into the titration cell to react completely with the iodine and hence decolorize the blue starch–iodine complex, the intensity of light transmitted by the solution increases sharply and causes a relay to open the burette valve and allow more iodate solution to be added to the titration cell. This regenerates more iodine and changes the colour of the solution back to blue. The relay now operates to stop the flow of titrant. The operations continue until no more iodate is delivered into the solution in a certain period of time, when it is concluded that no more sulphur dioxide will be produced.

2.9 Modifications of commercial photometers and spectrophotometers. No attempt will be made to describe all the modifications which have, at some time or other, been made to these instruments to convert them to titrators, since, basically, these modifications are all very similar. The conversion of an instrument is easily accomplished. It generally consists of replacing the usual holder for photometric cells in the cell compartment by the titration cell, which may often have dimensions only slightly less than those of the cell compartment itself. If a smaller titration cell is required, then it is a simple job to make a framework of wood, metal or plastic which will fit snugly into the cell compartment and hold the titration cell. The cell compartment cover is then replaced by a specially constructed cover which has holes drilled in it to take the burette and motor-driven stirring rod, if this type of stirrer is to be used. The jet of the burette should fit tightly into the cover, so that extraneous light does not get into the cell compartment through gaps left between the cover and the burette. It is also advisable to blacken that part of the burette between the cover and the lowest graduation mark to reduce extraneous light in the compartment to a minimum. The jet of the burette should also be drawn out to a sufficient length, so that the tip is always below the surface of the solution in the titration cell. It is also necessary to make sure no light enters the cell compartment by gaps which may exist between the stirring rod and the cover. This can easily be prevented by a simple device like the

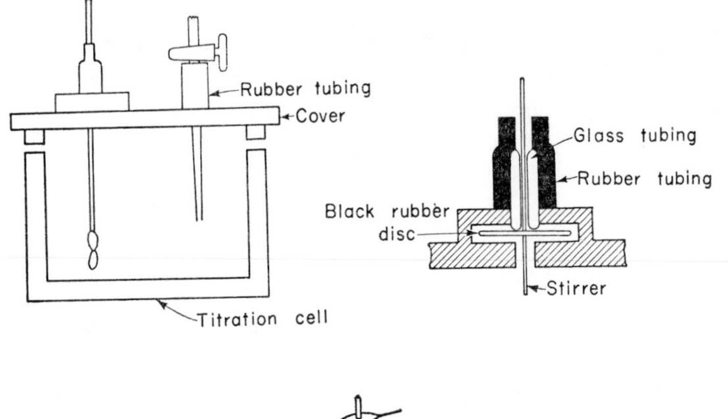

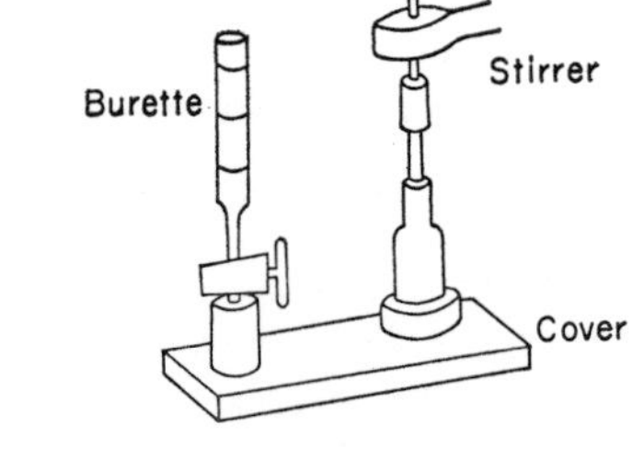

FIG. 17. An illustration of the accessories used with the Unicam SP 500 spectrophotometer for spectrophotometric titrations

one shown in Fig. 17 which illustrates the set-up used by Headridge and Magee[39] to convert the Unicam SP 500 for spectrophotometric titrations.

A magnetic stirrer may, of course, be used in place of a motor-driven stirring rod; the bottom of the cell compartment will then require slight modification, so that it can accommodate the motor for the rotating bar magnet which is situated immediately below the titration cell. The stirrer in the solution is usually a ferro-magnetic rod enclosed in glass or a suitable plastic material. With magnetic stirrers it should be borne in mind that the permanent magnet may have some slight effect on the photocell. Bricker and Schonberg[40] in determining vanadium (V) and chromium (VI) by spectrophotometric titration with iron (II) produced by photolytic reduction, have recommended that the magnetic stirrer should be shut off when optical density readings are being taken (see 8.3). In addition the magnet should always be orientated in the same direction with respect to the photocell when readings are taken, for Bricker and Schonberg found that the optical density changed by 0·008 depending on which pole of the magnet pointed towards the photocell.

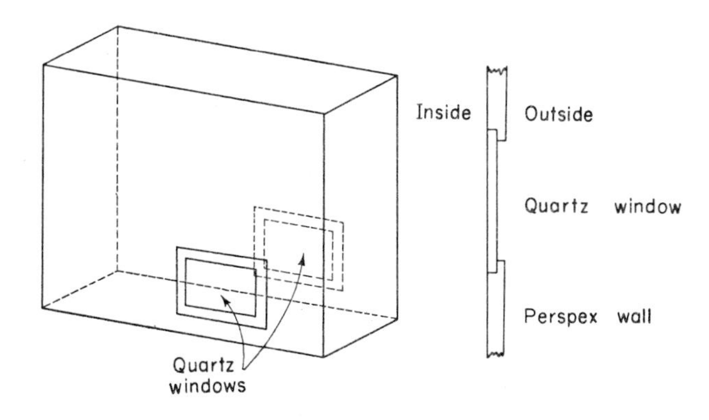

FIG. 18. A titration cell suitable for spectrophotometric titrations with ultra-violet light

With regard to the titration cell, it can be made of glass or a plastic such as Perspex, if light of wavelength greater than about 360 mμ is used. Often, beakers may be employed as titration cells. If optical density readings are to be taken with ultra-violet light ($\lambda < 360$ mμ) then the titration cell must be made, at least in part, from materials such as quartz which is transparent down to 200 mμ. Since quartz cells are much more expensive than glass or plastic cells it is often possible to construct a plastic cell with quartz windows inserted in such a way that the beam of light passes through the centre of them to the photoelectric cell. Such a cell was made by Headridge and Magee[39] for the Unicam SP 500 spectrophotometer and is shown in Fig. 18. The cell was constructed from 3 mm

Perspex sheet and contained two quartz windows made from a 3 in. × 1 in. fused silica microscope slide of 1 mm thickness, and sealed to the Perspex with Araldite 101 cold-setting resin mixed with Hardener 951 (supplied by Aero Research Ltd., Cambridge, England).

2.10 Many other instruments have been modified for manual photometric titrations, for example, the Coleman Model 14[41], Beckman Model B[20], Beckman Model DU[42, 43] and Unicam SP 600[44] spectrophotometers, and the EEL absorptiometer[45], a filter instrument. This list is by no means comprehensive. A few spectrophotometers have also been modified to record photometric titration curves automatically. These are the Cary recording spectrophotometer[46], the Beckman Model B spectrophotometer[47] and the Warren Spectracord[48]. Mullen and Anton[49] have also recently described an automatic recording spectrophotometric titrator built from a modified Beckman Model B spectrophotometer and a Precision-Dow recording potentiometric titrator. All of these titrators recorded a plot of optical density against volume of titrant added, but Chalmers and Walley[50] preferred to locate the end-point by recording the rate of change of optical density, i.e. the first derivative of optical density with respect to volume of titrant added. Their titrator was constructed using a Unicam SP 600 spectrophotometer. An interesting account of automatic photometric titrators is given by J. P. Phillips in his book on automatic titrators[51].

2.11 It is also possible to make additions of titrant to a solution outside the cell compartment of a photometer or spectrophotometer, if a circulatory system with pump is employed. The cell compartment then holds a flow-through cell, through which the solution is constantly passing. Titrant is added at some other point in the system. With these systems equilibrium can be reached in 5 to 20 sec. This method has been used with the Hilger Spekker absorptiometer[52], the Beckman Model B spectrophotometer[53, 54], the Beckman Model DU spectrophotometer[54, 55], the Cary recording spectrophotometer[54] and the Bausch and Lomb Spectronic 20 colorimeter[54].

2.12 Instruments constructed from basic components. A photometric titrator can be readily built from basic components, and until 1950 all photometric titrators were constructed in this manner. However, since 1954 most photometric titrations reported in the chemical literature have been performed on modified commercial photometers or spectrophotometers. Even so, a few workers have preferred to build their own equipment. A typical example is the heterometer constructed by Bobtelsky to study precipitation titrations[56]. This consisted of a vertical glass cylinder of about 4 cm diameter with a plane base, which contained the solution that was to be titrated. The volume of the solution was generally 10–20 ml. A vertical glass stirrer and the burette tip were immersed into the solution from above. The glass cell was surrounded with a metallic jacket through which water could flow at 20°C in order to maintain the solution at a constant temperature. The light source was a 3–5 watt flashlight bulb which was suspended above the titration cell. Light from the source passed through the solution and through a filter and diaphragm below the titration cell to the photoelectric cell. The current produced from the photocell was recorded on a galvanometer. The optical density values were then calculated from the galvanometer readings. A special feature about this instrument is the vertical illumination. In precipitation titrations, even with fast stirring, there is sometimes a tendency for the particles to fall to the lower part of the titration cell. This "settling out" effect can lead to erroneous results if a horizontal light beam is passed through the solution. With a vertical light beam the effect of particles settling out is greatly reduced.

Shapiro and Brannock[57] and Bril and co-workers[58] have also built their own recording titrators. The Shapiro instrument consisted of a Mariotte bottle to deliver the titrant at a constant rate, a titrator and a pen-and-ink recorder. The titrator was of simple construction and contained a light bulb, suitable lenses, the titration beaker, a filter holder, a barrier layer selenium photocell and a magnetic stirrer. The titration apparatus of the Bril instrument consisted of a light source, a condenser lens, a light filter, a titration beaker, a motor-driven stirrer and a photovoltaic cell. The output of the photocell was recorded on a spot galvanometer and the movement of the spot was followed by means of a photoelectric recorder. The titrant was added at about 0·3 ml/min from a 5 ml microburette, and a special switch and circuit were incorporated in the recording system such that a small electric current could be superimposed momentarily on the recorded photocurrent when the switch was depressed manually every 0·1 ml. This produced marks on the paper which greatly facilitated the accurate location of the equivalence point.

Photoelectric relay titrators may also be readily constructed from basic components. In fact, the first photometric titrator built by Müller and Partridge[3] was of this type. Phillips[59] has given instructions for the construction of a simple automatic titrator incorporating a relay to terminate the flow of titrant at the end-point. His paper should be consulted for details of the instrument. The commercial CENCO and Stone Titrators are, of course, photoelectric relay titrators.

2.13 Modifications of automatic potentiometric titrators. A high impedance automatic potentiometric titrator can be modified for automatic photometric titrations by connecting the terminals, usually attached to electrodes, across a large resistance in series with a vacuum phototube and its power supply. The photocell should be situated in a titration unit along with a light source, filter holder, titration cell, stirrer and burette. For solutions containing an added indicator, a plot of potential difference across the resistance against volume of titrant added has a shape similar to that of a normal potentiometric titration curve, provided that there is a sharp change in colour at the equivalence point. The large change in potential difference which is obtained at the equivalence point operates a relay to stop the addition of titrant. A commercial instrument which has been modified for photometric titrations is the Beckman Model K automatic potentiometric titrator[60].

CHAPTER 3

ACID-BASE TITRATIONS

3.1 Until 1954, photometric end-point detection was employed only occasionally in acid-base titrations. For the systems investigated before that time, a visual, potentiometric or conductometric titration was usually satisfactory without having to resort to other means of end-point detection.

For titration of strong acids and bases, a photometric titration is seldom necessary because most pH indicators, having high molar extinction coefficients, are used in very low concentrations and sharp visual end-points are almost always obtained. However, with these systems, visual end-point detection may become difficult when the original solution is dark coloured[1] or very dilute[61] and photometric titrations have been carried out to overcome these difficulties. With neutralization reactions, photometric end-point detection undoubtedly finds its main use in the titration of weak acids and bases.

Even in the last six years, only a few papers have appeared on the photometric titration of acids and bases where an indicator is added, the most interesting of these having originated from Higuchi and his co-workers[25, 26, 28] who made use of theoretical equations in their work.

Other recent papers on the photometric titration of acids and bases deal with self-indicator systems. Because weak acids and their conjugate bases, and weak bases and their conjugate acids, absorb mainly in the ultra-violet region of the spectrum, these methods have only been developed since spectrophotometers, which could give essentially monochromatic ultra-violet radiation, became generally available.

These researches in recent years have shown that photometric titration is a most useful technique for the determination of very weak acids and bases, because, for this class of compounds, visual end-point detection is seldom satisfactory and potentiometric and conductometric titration often unreliable.

Applications

Titrations in self-indicator systems

3.2 Telluric acid. To determine telluric acid in aqueous solution, Leonard and Henry[62] titrated spectrophotometrically with ammonium hydroxide solution. The method is feasible since the tellurate ion, in this case $H_5TeO_6^-$, absorbs at a longer wavelength than telluric acid. The optimum wavelength for the titration depends on the concentration of the telluric acid but lies between 250 and 280 mμ. In a conical flask, 50 ml of solution containing 11–445 mg of telluric acid were titrated with 2 N ammonium hydroxide solution and, after the addition of each volume increment of titrant, the optical density of the solution was measured in a 1 cm quartz cell in a spectrophotometer. A plot of optical density, corrected if necessary for volume change, against volume of titrant added gave the end-point.

It would be much more convenient to carry out this titration in the cell compartment of a spectrophotometer. Since the length of the light path through the solution could then be, say 6 cm, the sensitivity of the method would be increased so that as little as 2 mg of telluric acid could be titrated.

Leonard and Henry showed that telluric acid could also be determined in the presence of stronger acids such as hydrochloric, selenic and acetic acids. The solution does not absorb appreciably until the strong acid has been titrated.

3.3 Phenols. Goddu and Hume[24], in experiments to verify their theoretically-derived titration plots (1.10), have titrated spectrophotometrically phenols in aqueous solution with carbonate-free 0·1 M aqueous sodium hydroxide solution. Since phenolate anions absorb at longer wavelengths than phenols themselves, a wavelength was chosen where, for the phenol to be titrated, only the phenolate anion absorbed. In solutions as dilute as 10^{-3} M good results were obtained with phenols of $pK_A \leqslant 9{\cdot}2$. The method is also suitable for titrating mixtures of a strong acid and a phenol, and also mixtures of phenols where there is a reasonable difference in their pK values.

Procedure. Transfer about 100 ml of aqueous solution containing 0·2–0·4 milliequivalents of a phenol to a suitable cell for a spectrophotometric titration. Set the stirrer in motion and pass nitrogen through the solution to exclude carbon dioxide. Select a wavelength at which the phenolate anion will absorb, and the phenol will not absorb appreciably, and adjust the optical density scale reading to zero. Add the titrant from a 5 ml microburette in 0·2 ml increments until all of the phenol is titrated. When neutralization is complete the readings will remain at a steady value. Make a plot of optical density against volume of titrant added and by the usual method of extrapolation locate the end-point.

McKinney and Reynolds[63] have titrated spectrophotometrically phenols in butylamine with a 0·05 M solution of sodium hydroxide in absolute ethanol. Phenol, 8-hydroxyquinoline, methyl salicylate and 2:4:6-trichlorophenol were among the compounds satisfactorily titrated. In cases where the acidities of two phenols were sufficiently different, a differential titration was used to determine both phenols, the phenol which was the strongest acid being titrated first.

Procedure. This is identical to the method used above by Goddu and Hume except that approximately 0·1 m-equiv. of a phenol in about 100 ml of butylamine are titrated.

3.4 Organic bases. Reilley and Schweizer[14] have applied spectrophotometric titration to the determination of weak organic bases in glacial acetic acid using 0·1 N perchloric acid in glacial acetic acid as titrant. These titrations are possible since most weak organic bases and their conjugate acids have different absorption spectra. Examples of the bases titrated are quinoline and *o*-chloroaniline. They also showed that differential titrations of mixtures of a strong base and a weak base were possible.

Procedure. Transfer about 100 ml of glacial acetic acid containing approximately 1 m-equiv. of base to the cell of a spectrophotometric titrator and select a suitable wavelength for the titration such that there will be either a rise or fall in the optical density of the solution as the base is titrated. Set the optical density scale reading to zero if a rise is expected and to 1·0 or other suitable value if the reverse will occur. Set the stirrer in motion and add the titrant in 1 ml increments or less. Correct the optical density readings for volume change and determine the end-point from the usual plot.

The method of Reilley and Schweizer, just described, has been extended by Hummelstedt and Hume[64] to the titration of a wide range of organic bases and to mixtures of up to four organic bases. They employed 0·5 M perchloric acid in acetic acid as titrant. For the titration of all but the weakest bases, the solution need not be anhydrous and is readily prepared by dissolving 72% perchloric acid in glacial acetic acid. If the aqueous pK_B value is < 10 the base cannot be determined by direct photometric titration in acetic acid because it is completely protonated by the solvent. However a titration in a non-acidic solvent such as acetonitrile is satisfactory. For the titration of very weak bases, $pK_B \simeq 13$ in water, acetic acid must be used as solvent. For aqueous pK_B values $\geqslant 14$ for the base, the method is no longer applicable, non-linearity in the plot being too extensive to allow an extrapolation to the end-point. For the photometric titration of these extremely weak bases the methods of Higuchi *et al.*[25, 26, 28] (1.12, 1.13 and 1.14) must be applied.

3.5 Aluminium 8-hydroxyquinolinate. This compound in glacial acetic acid has been titrated spectrophotometrically at 450 mμ with a 0·1 N solution of acetous perchloric acid[65]. The optical density of the solution decreases as perchloric acid is added. The method may be employed for the determination of 0·5–10 mg of aluminium.

Titrations with indicator added

3.6 Automatic titrations. Several workers[34, 36, 37, 49, 50], have carried out acid-base titrations automatically with photometric or spectrophotometric titrators built in their laboratories to determine the capabilities of the instruments. Since these acid-base titrations are of the usual type where a visual end-point is generally employed and have no special features which make a photometric titration particularly necessary, they will not be discussed in detail. As mentioned previously in Chapter 2, titrations can be terminated automatically by making use of a photometer to detect a sharp change in optical density at the end-point, but it must be realized that many titrations can be terminated automatically by other means, for example, by potentiometric end-point detection. While it is an aim of this monograph to record most of the information which has been published about methods based on or related to photometric titration, its primary function is to discuss the application of photometric titration to those systems where it is particularly useful, and where there are distinct advantages in employing the technique. Hence, little or no mention will be made of photometric titrations performed merely to test out an instrument.

An application of automatic photometric titration which was of great interest was that made by James and Martin[66] for the determination of volatile fatty acids that had been separated by vapour phase chromatography. In their paper, which launched this important analytical technique, they were able to separate and determine quantitatively mixtures of fatty acids from formic acid to dodecanoic acid. The separated fatty acids in the gas phase were absorbed in water in a titration cell where they were continuously titrated with sodium hydroxide solution, the indicator being phenol red. When a fatty acid was absorbed in the solution in the cell, the pH of the solution fell and the colour of the indicator changed from red to

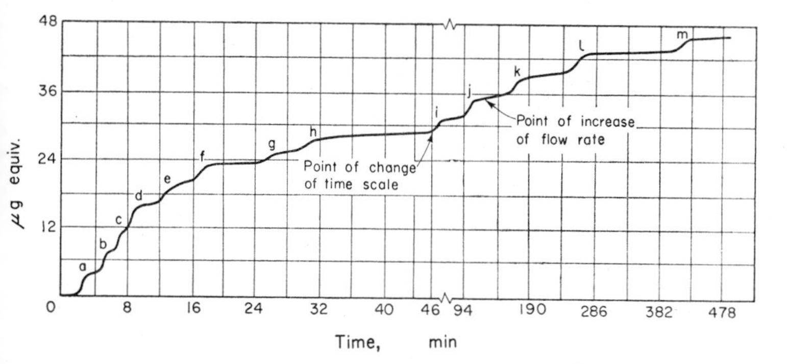

FIG. 19. The separation of (a) acetic, (b) propionic, (c) n-butyric, (d) iso-butyric, (e) n-valeric, (f) commercial "iso-valeric", (g) γ-methyl-valeric, (h) hexanoic, (i) heptanoic, (j) octanoic, (k) nonanoic, (l) decanoic, and (m) hendecanoic acids. Column length, 4 ft; liquid phase, stearic acid (10% w/w) in DC 550 silicone; nitrogen pressure, 47 cm Hg; flow-rate 18·2 ml/min; temp. 137°C. At the time indicated by the second arrow the pressure was increased to 76·5 cm Hg and the flow rate to 35 ml/min

yellow. This colour change caused titrant to flow into the cell until the pH was restored to its original value, when the colour of the solution changed back to red and the addition of titrant ceased. A plot of quantity of alkali added (μg equiv.) against time was recorded automatically. Figure 19 shows such a plot for the separation of a number of fatty acids.

James and co-workers[67] used the same apparatus to separate and determine ammonia, aliphatic amines and homologues of pyridine. 0·04 N sulphuric acid was the titrant and methyl red the indicator. These separations of organic acids and bases by vapour phase chromatography were also reported elsewhere[68].

Malmstadt and Vassallo[69] have employed automatic derivative photometric end-point detection for the direct titration of hydrochloric–sulphuric acid and nitric–sulphuric acid mixtures in acetone as solvent. The apparatus consisted of a special stand for photometric titrations in conjunction with the Sargent–Malmstadt derivative control unit. (The commercial Sargent–Malmstadt automatic spectro-electro titrator (2.6) has obviously been developed from this instrument.)

About 1 m-equiv. of the mixed acids in 50 ml of 98% acetone in a suitable titration cell were titrated automatically with 0·1 N tri-n-butylmethylammonium hydroxide in benzene containing a little methanol. An interference filter was used to select a wavelength of 575 mμ. Neutral red and thymolphthalein were the indicators. At the first end-point which corresponded to the titration of the hydrogen ion from hydrochloric or nitric acid with one of the hydrogen ions from the sulphuric acid, a sharp decrease in optical density occurred as the neutral red changed from red to yellow. At the second end-point which corresponded to the titration of the second hydrogen ion from the sulphuric acid, the optical density increased sharply as the thymolphthalein changed from yellow to green.

Automatic derivative spectrophotometric titration has also been applied to the determination of a range of organic acids in solvents containing at least 90% acetone[70]. The titrant was again tri-n-butyl methylammonium hydroxide and titrations were performed on the Sargent–Malmstadt automatic spectro-electro titrator with the use of suitable indicators.

3.7 Boron tribromide and its addition compounds. Schuele *et al.*[71] applied visual, potentiometric, conductometric and spectrophotometric titrations to the analysis of boron tribromide and its addition compounds with organic bases, and found that spectrophotometric titrations were the most satisfactory.

To analyse an addition compound a weighed quantity was dissolved in water and the base removed on a column of the cation exchange resin, Amberlite IR 100, in the hydrogen form. An aliquot of the effluent from the column which contained hydrobromic and boric acids was titrated spectrophotometrically with sodium hydroxide solution using methyl red or a mixed indicator of methyl red and methylene blue for the titration of the hydrobromic acid and phenolphthalein for the titration of boric acid after the addition of mannitol. Before the titrations were started the instrument was adjusted so that the transmission increased from approximately 10% to 90% or vice versa during the titration and the end-point was then taken at 50% transmission. However, the end-point could probably have been determined more satisfactorily from a plot of optical density against volume of titrant added.

3.8 Carbon dioxide in gases. Spectrophotometric titration has been employed for the determination of parts per million of carbon dioxide in gases[61]. The carbon dioxide in the sample of gas was absorbed in 0·0001 N sodium hydroxide solution in a special absorption bulb and the excess of sodium hydroxide back-titrated with 0·002 N hydrochloric acid solution using phenolphthalein as indicator. The end-point was obtained in the usual manner from a plot of optical density against volume of titrant added. A spectrophotometric titration was employed because a visual end-point was difficult with solutions of such low concentration.

3.9 Weak organic acids and bases. Higuchi *et al.*[25] have titrated an aqueous solution of benzoic acid spectrophotometrically at 615 mμ with aqueous sodium hydroxide solution using bromothymol blue as indicator, and have determined the end-point with great precision by employing the type of plot described in section 1.12. The ratio of the concentration of the indicator in the acidic form to its concentration in the basic form, calculated for optical density readings just before the end-point, was plotted against volume of titrant added. The end-point occurred at the intersection of the straight line plot on the volume axis. A similar procedure was used for the titration of triphenylguanidine in glacial acetic acid with acetous perchloric acid employing quinaldine red as indicator. These titrations proved that the end-point could be located very precisely using the special type of plot, but, as the authors state, this type of plot will only produce precise results for the titration of a weak acid if $pK_I \gg pK_A$. When this is so, a visual titration is generally satisfactory anyway so there is no advantage in using a photometric titration and the special type of plot, unless very high precision in end-point location is required.

However, when $pK_I \simeq pK_A$, the type of plot described in section 1.13 may be employed. For the titration of a weak acid, the ratio of the concentration of the indicator in the acidic form to its concentration in the basic form, $[IH^+]/[I]$, is plotted against the reciprocal of the volume added (abscissa). The straight line plot intersects the abscissa at the reciprocal of the stoichiometrically required amount of standard base. If a weak base is titrated with a strong acid, then the ratio of the concentration of the indicator in the basic form to its concentration in the acidic form [I]/[IH+], is used as the ordinate.

Higuchi and co-workers[25] employed this second type of plot for the location of the end-point after a spectrophotometric titration of urea in glacial acetic acid with acetous perchloric acid using malachite green or Nile Blue A as indicator. For this type of system a photometric titration is necessary, for a visual end-point is impossible and a potentiometric titration unsatisfactory.

Procedure. Dissolve a quantity of material containing 0·2–0·5 g of urea in approximately 50 ml of glacial acetic acid in a 100 ml graduated flask, and add 10 ml of 0·01 % acetous malachite green solution. Make the volume exactly 100 ml with glacial acetic acid. Pipette 20 ml of solution into a suitable titration cell for a spectrophotometer, adjust the wavelength to 622 mμ and set the stirrer in motion. Select a suitable optical density reading and titrate the solution with acetous perchloric acid solution containing the same concentration of indicator. Record optical density readings every 0·2 ml until a minimum optical density reading is obtained. From the optical density readings calculate values of [I]/[IH+] and plot these against the reciprocal volume of titrant added. Locate the end-point by the method described above. If Nile Blue A is used as indicator the titration should be made at 632 mμ.

Recently Karsten and co-workers[72] have applied this type of plot to the photometric titration of about 1 m-equiv. amounts of a number of sodium salts of organic acids in about 100 ml of glacial acetic acid with 0·1 N acetous perchloric acid using methyl violet as indicator at 546 mμ. Among the compounds titrated satisfactorily were sodium benzoate, sodium salicylate and sodium glycerophosphate. *K*-values (K_A/K_I) varied from 0·008 to 0·093 showing that this type of plot may also be employed for systems where $K < 0{\cdot}05$. Higuchi *et al.*[25] used this plot only for systems where $K > 0{\cdot}05$.

Rehm and Higuchi[26] have also employed a third type of plot (1.14) for the titration of very weak bases with strong acids where an even weaker base is used as indicator. Here the indicator changes colour primarily after all of the base has been titrated and data obtained from optical density readings well past the end-point are used. The ratio of the concentration of the indicator in the acidic form to the concentration in the basic form is plotted against volume of titrant added; extrapolating the straight line plot back to the volume axis gives the end-point.

Higuchi's first two types of plots (1.12 and 1.13) when applied to the titration of weak bases were based on an equation which described the competition of the base and the indicator for hydrogen ions derived from the strong acid. It was assumed that competition from the solvent in the system for hydrogen ions was negligible before the end-point. With this third type of plot, however, the basic equation describes the competition of the indicator and solvent for hydrogen ions derived from the strong acid. It is obvious that this type of plot can only be applied to systems where the indicator is an extremely weak base, i.e. comparable to the solvent in basic strength. With such systems visual end-point detection cannot be applied. If the base to be determined is itself very weak, accurate end-point location by potentiometric or conductometric titration is very difficult; reasonable results can only be obtained by a photometric titration.

With this type of plot, Rehm and Higuchi[26] have determined sodium acetate, sodium benzoate, aniline and pyridine in aqueous solution with hydrochloric acid as titrant and metanil yellow as indicator. Urea, antipyrine and N-methylpyrrolidine in glacial acetic acid were also titrated with acetous perchloric acid using Sudan III as indicator.

Recently Connors and Higuchi[28] have reported that with their second type of plot (1.13), deviations from linearity occur for the titration of weak bases in acetic acid when small quantities of base are taken. These deviations are caused by solvolysis of the salt formed during the titration. (A straight line plot had been predicted theoretically on the assumption that solvolysis of the salt formed was negligible, but with very weak bases this is not so.) These workers have therefore modified their original equation to take account of solvolytic effects. The original paper should be consulted for more detail. By a modified type of plot, sample sizes in the range of 20–30 mg can be determined with good precision and accuracy. Among the bases titrated with acetous perchloric acid were acetamide, urea and caffeine. Nile Blue A, *p*-naphtholbenzein and malachite green were used as indicators.

CHAPTER 4

OXIDATION-REDUCTION SYSTEMS

4.1 Many of the early oxidation-reduction photometric titrations were made on systems where it seems likely that a visual end-point would have been faster and equally satisfactory. Admittedly these titrations were often performed to test the usefulness of a home-made instrument. An example is the photometric titration of ferrous ions with permanganate, which has been reported on several occasions. In this titration the visual end-point is usually perfectly satisfactory and a photometric titration is unnecessary. These photometric titrations which appear to possess no advantages over visual titrations will not be reported here.

However, there are times when photometric end-point detection may be applied with advantage to familiar oxidation-reduction titrations which are generally followed visually; and that is when the solutions are deeply coloured owing to the presence of certain foreign ions. In these cases visual end-point detection may become difficult. Some early workers were aware of these facts. Somiya and Yasuda[73], for example, have determined iron in green nickel sulphate solution by photometric titration of the iron in the ferrous state with standard potassium permanganate solution. Manganese has also been determined in nickel steel by photometric titration of the manganese as permanganate with arsenite solution[74].

With the advent of commercial spectrophotometers, however, the way was open to achieve readily, spectrophotometric oxidation-reduction titrations which were not amenable to visual end-point detection and the majority of the titrations described in the following sections are of this type.

4.2 Antimony. Antimony (III) in sulphuric acid solution has been determined by spectrophotometric titration with standard bromate–bromide solution[16]. At 296–330 mμ, antimony (III) and (V), bromide and sulphate ions do not absorb appreciably but the tribromide ion absorbs strongly. The end-point is therefore located on the plot of optical density against volume of titrant added, at the intersection of a horizontal straight line before the end-point with a steeply rising straight line after the end-point. 3–30 mg of antimony were determined with results accurate to within 2 parts per thousand.

Antimony (III) was also determined in hydrochloric acid solution but the method is not quite so convenient since the antimony (III) chloro complex absorbs strongly in the region, 296–330 mμ, and the choice of the initial optical density setting then depends on the amount of antimony present. Arsenic (III) chloride does not, however, absorb appreciably in this wavelength range, and the determination of mixtures of arsenic (III) and antimony (III) by photometric titration is possible. This determination is described in section 4.3.

Procedure. Transfer an aliquot of solution containing 3–30 mg of antimony (III) to a suitable spectrophotometric titration cell and dilute to about 80 ml with appropriate solutions such that the final solution is 2–3 N in sulphuric acid and 1·5% (w/v) in potassium bromide. Set the wavelength to a value in the range of 296–330 mμ depending on the amount of antimony that is to be expected. (A wavelength of 330 mμ is suitable for 30 mg of antimony. Progressively lower wavelengths should be chosen for progressively smaller amounts of antimony.) Set the stirrer in motion and adjust the optical density reading to zero. Titrate the solution with 0·1 N bromate–bromide solution (M/60 potassium bromate + M/12 potassium bromide) for 10–30 mg amounts of antimony, and with 0·01 N titrant for smaller quantities of the metal. Locate the end-point graphically in the usual way.

4.3 Arsenic. Bricker and Sweetser[42] have determined arsenic (III) in sulphuric acid solution by spectrophotometric titration with ceric sulphate at 320 mμ. Only the ceric ions absorb appreciably at this wavelength. 50 μg–35 mg amounts of arsenic were determined with an average error not exceeding 0·2%. The concentration of the titrant varied from 4×10^{-4} M to 0·1 M depending on the amount of arsenic that was to be titrated.

Procedure. Add an aliquot of solution containing 50 μg to 35 mg of arsenic (III) to a suitable cell for a spectrophotometric titration and dilute to 100 ml with sulphuric acid and water so that the final solution is 1·0 to 1·2 N with respect to sulphuric acid. Add 3 or 4 drops of 0·01 M osmium tetroxide solution to act as a catalyst in the oxidation. Set the wavelength to 320 mμ, start the stirrer into motion and adjust the optical density reading to zero. Titrate the solution with standard ceric sulphate solution of a suitable concentration, noting the optical density readings after the addition of small increments of titrant, and locate the end-point from the usual plot.

Arsenic (III) has also been titrated spectrophotometrically with bromate–bromide solution[16]. The method is identical to the one already described for antimony (III) in section 4.2. 2–25 mg of arsenic were determined with an average error of less than 0·2%.

With mixtures of arsenic (III) and antimony (III), the arsenic is titrated before the antimony with bromate–bromide solution, but arsenic and antimony cannot be determined separately by a spectrophotometric titration at 296–330 mμ in sulphuric acid solution, because in this wavelength region only the tribromide ion absorbs and the plot of optical density against volume of titrant added shows only one break; that is when both arsenic and antimony have been titrated. However, it is possible to determine each of these elements in a mixture if the titration is made in 6–7 N hydrochloric acid solution at 326 mμ. At this wavelength the antimony (III) chloro complex, as well as the tribromide ion, absorb strongly. The other ions present during the titration do not absorb appreciably. A plot of optical density against volume of titrant added therefore consists of three lines, a horizontal line of high optical density as the arsenic (III) is titrated, a line of decreasing optical density as the antimony (III) chloro complex is oxidized and finally a line of increasing optical density as the concentration of the tribromide ion builds up when both arsenic (III) and antimony (III) have been titrated.

The first break corresponds to the amount of arsenic in the solution. The volume of titrant added between the first and second breaks is a measure of the antimony in the solution. About 10 mg amounts of both arsenic and antimony were titrated in hydrochloric acid medium. The maximum error for each constituent was less than 2%.

Bapat and Tatwawadi[75] have indicated that sodium arsenite in 10–15% (w/v) sodium hydroxide solution may be determined by photometric titration at about 460 mμ with standard potassium ferricyanide solution but they give very few details. After the end-point, when all of the arsenic (III) is oxidized to arsenic (V), the optical density readings of the solution increase as excess ferricyanide is added.

Bapat and Tatwawadi[75] have also titrated photometrically with standard iodate solution, arsenic (III) in hydrochloric acid solution containing mercuric chloride. In 0·5–3 N hydrochloric acid solutions the arsenic (III) was oxidized to arsenic (V) and the iodate reduced to iodide. This latter reaction was assisted by the formation of the stable tetra-iodomercury (II) ion. After the end-point in the titration, the excess of iodate then oxidized the iodide in the tetra-iodomercury (II) ion to iodine. Titrations were performed at about 475 mμ where iodine absorbs appreciably. As expected the optical density of the solution remains at zero until the end-point and then increases steadily after the end-point. The end-point could be located from a plot of optical density against volume of titrant added.

In this system it was also possible to titrate the iodide from the tetra-iodomercury (II) ion, which was, of course, equivalent to the amount of arsenic (III) originally present, to iodine monochloride with more iodate if the hydrochloric acid concentration was between 1 and 6 N. The iodide is initially oxidized to iodine, which is then further oxidized to iodine monochloride. The optical density therefore rises as the concentration of iodine in the solution increases and then falls steadily to the second end-point, after which the optical density readings are constant. The titrant itself is reduced to iodine monochloride.

About 5 mg amounts of arsenic (III) were determined with a maximum error of 3%. More work will have to be done on this system if iodate is to serve as a volumetric reagent for arsenic (III) using photometric end-point detection.

In addition, Bapat and Tatwawadi appear to have operated their instrument, a Hilger Spekker absorptiometer, incorrectly. They state that in the oxidation of iodide (from tetra-iodomercury (II) ion) to iodine monochloride, the optical density of the solution falls as iodine is produced. Surely this cannot be the case.

4.4 Cerium. Bricker and Loeffler[12] have determined cerium (III) by spectrophotometric titration at 400 mμ with standard cobalt (III) sulphate solution. A plot of optical density against volume of titrant added gave a line rising from zero optical density at the start of the titration to a high optical density value at the end-point, because the cerium (IV) produced in the oxidation absorbs strongly at 400 mμ. After the end-point the optical density values rise only very slowly, owing to the slight absorption of the excess of cobalt (III) sulphate. At this wavelength cobalt (II) and cerium (III) ions scarcely absorb.

1·7–6·7 mg of cerium (III) were determined with a precision of about 5 parts in a 1000, but the accuracy of the method was in doubt since the amount of cerium recovered was 1·5% higher than the quantity taken as determined by the sodium bismuthate method[76]. The sodium bismuthate method may, however, have given low results for the cerium determinations. Obviously the reliability of this spectrophotometric titration should be checked with a standard cerium (III) solution prepared, say, from a weighed quantity of the pure metal.

The cobalt (III) sulphate solution was obtained by anodic

oxidation of a saturated solution of cobalt (II) sulphate in 10 N sulphuric acid, which itself had been prepared at 0°C. An appropriate quantity of the slurry of dark green cobalt (III) sulphate crystals and solution, thus obtained, was diluted so that the final solution was approximately 0·01 M and 18 N with respect to sulphuric acid. This solution was quite stable when stored at −7°C. Oxidation of the water in the solution was negligible during a period of a few minutes at room temperature. The cobalt (III) sulphate solution was standardized against standard ferrous ammonium sulphate solution using spectrophotometric end-point detection. The method used for this standardization was identical to the procedure described in section 4.12 where iron (II) is determined by spectrophotometric titration with standard cobalt (III) solution, except that a known amount of ferrous ion was titrated with the cobalt (III) sulphate solution to be standardized.

Procedure. Add an aliquot of solution containing 1·5–7 mg of cerium (III) to the spectrophotometric titration cell and adjust the volume to 90 ml with 1 M sulphuric acid. Then add 10 drops of 0·1 M silver nitrate solution as a catalyst for the oxidation. Fill the burette with the titrant and allow to stand for 5 min so that the temperature of the solution approaches room temperature. Set the wavelength to 400 mμ, start the stirrer into motion and adjust the optical density reading to zero. Titrate the solution with 0·01 M cobalt (III) sulphate solution, but do not record optical density readings until about 1 ml before the end-point, because the addition of 18 N sulphuric acid to the approximately N acid in the cell causes a rise in temperature with a subsequent slight increase in absorption of the cerium (IV) ions. This phenomenon can introduce errors in end-point location, unless only those optical density values in the vicinity of the end-point are recorded. Locate the end-point from the usual plot of optical density against volume of titrant added.

Cerium (III) has also been determined in neutral pyrophosphate medium by spectrophotometric titration at 525 mμ with standard potassium permanganate solution[77]. The cerium (III) is oxidized to cerium (IV) while the permanganate is reduced to the manganese (III) pyrophosphate complex. The cerium and manganese pyrophosphate complexes are soluble. A visual end-point is obscured by the pale violet colour of the manganese (III) pyrophosphate complex. A plot of optical density against volume of titrant added consists of two lines, one of small gradient before the end-point and the other of steep gradient after the end-point. This shape of plot is obtained since the manganese (III) complex absorbs only slightly at 525 mμ, while the permanganate ion absorbs strongly. Other ions in the solution do not absorb or have a constant absorption.

5–90 mg amounts of cerium (III) were determined with an average error of less than 2 parts in 1000. The precision was good, the coefficient of variation being 0·4%. Large amounts of ceric ion cause no interference nor do appreciable amounts of aluminium, iron (III), cobalt (II), molybdenum (VI), vanadium (V), tungsten (VI), thorium, chloride, bromide, copper (II) and nickel. Iron (II) can be oxidized to iron (III) by bubbling air through the solution before the titration. Tin (II) does not interfere if optical density readings after the end-point are measured quickly. Interference occurs with the reducing agents, mercury (I), arsenic (III), antimony (III), thallium (I), vanadium (IV) and iodide. Fluoride and chromium (III) also interfere.

Procedure. Add 75 ml of a filtered solution of tetrapotassium pyrophosphate (11·5% w/v) to a suitable spectrophotometric titration cell and add 1 M sulphuric acid until the pH is between 5·5 and 7·0. Add 1–10 ml of the solution to be analysed which should contain 5–90 mg of cerium (III) and readjust the pH of the solution if necessary. Set the wavelength to 525 mμ, start the stirrer and adjust the optical density reading to zero. Titrate in the usual way with standard permanganate solution, 0·003–0·03 M depending on the amount of cerium to be titrated, and locate the end-point from the plot of optical density against volume of titrant added.

Note. Edwards and Milner[78] have applied this method of Marple and co-workers[77] to the determination of cerium in alloys containing bismuth and/or uranium. A filter photometer was modified for photometric titrations. Good results were obtained. Neither bismuth nor uranium interfered in the method.

4.5 Chromium. Miles and Englis[79] have determined mixtures of chromium and vanadium by spectrophotometric titration. The chromium, as dichromate, was first titrated selectively with standard arsenious acid solution which reduced only the chromium (VI) but not the vanadium (V). The vanadium, as vanadic acid, was then determined by titration with standard ferrous sulphate solution. The titrations were made at 350 mμ. At this wavelength the dichromate ions absorb strongly and the vanadic acid appreciably, but other ions present during the titration do not absorb or have a constant absorption. Iron (III) in sulphuric acid solution absorbs strongly at 350 mμ, but its absorption at this wavelength is greatly reduced by the addition of orthophosphoric acid. During the titration with arsenious acid solution, the optical density readings decrease as the dichromate is reduced, and become steady when this reduction is complete. When the solution is then titrated with ferrous sulphate, the optical density readings again decrease to the second end-point as the vanadic acid is reduced to vanadium (IV).

Mixtures containing 1·7–17·3 mg of chromium and 2·4–4·8 mg of vanadium were analysed for their metal content. The maximum errors for the chromium and vanadium recoveries were + 1% and −1% respectively. The results were fairly satisfactory, but indicated that a very small amount of vanadium (V) was being reduced along with the chromium (VI) by the arsenious acid. The method was also applied with good results to the determination of these elements in a steel.

These workers also stated that dichromate and vanadic acid, when present separately, may be satisfactorily determined by spectrophotometric titration with standard ferrous sulphate solution, but no results were given.

Procedure for mixtures of chromium (VI) and vanadium (V). Add an aliquot of solution containing up to 20 mg of chromium (VI) and up to 5 mg of vanadium (V) to a suitable titration cell and add 6 ml of 85% phosphoric acid and 2 ml of concentrated sulphuric acid dissolved in 10 ml of water. Dilute the solution with water to about 50 ml. Set the wavelength to 350 mμ, start the stirrer into motion and adjust the optical density readings to a suitable high value. Add standard 0·1 N arsenious acid solution in 0·2 ml increments. The reaction is slow near the end-point and time must be allowed for the system to come to equilibrium. After the addition of about 1 ml of arsenious acid solution past the first end-point, as shown by the constancy of optical density, titrate the solution with standard 0·1 N ferrous sulphate solution in the same manner. Correct the optical density readings for dilution and locate the two end-points from a plot of optical density against volume of titrant added.

4.6 Cobalt. Nickel sulphate crystals have been analysed for cobalt by photometric titration of a de-aerated ammoniacal pyrophosphate solution, with standard hydrogen peroxide solution[73]. The red cobalt (II) complex was oxidized to a violet cobalt (III) complex. Photometric end-point detection was satisfactory.

4.7 Copper. Malmstadt and Hadjiioannou[80] have determined copper in certain metallurgical products by automatic derivative photometric titration. The Sargent–Malmstadt spectro-electro titrator (2.6) was used. A suitable aliquot of the alloy solution, from which lead, manganese, and tin had been removed as hydroxide by precipitation with ammonium hydroxide, was buffered at pH 4·0 with acetic acid and sodium acetate and treated with potassium iodide crystals. Iodine and cuprous iodide were produced. On stirring, the cuprous iodide dissolved with the formation of a complex iodide anion. The iodine, equivalent to the copper in the solution, was then titrated with standard sodium thiosulphate solution. The disappearance of the absorption band of the triiodide ion between 350 and 400 mμ provided the signal for the termination of the titration.

An aliquot of alloy solution was then titrated automatically for the sum of copper and zinc with standard EDTA solution using 1-(2-pyridylazo)-2-naphthol as indicator (see section 5.7—Malmstadt and Hadjiioannou). The amount of zinc in the alloy was obtained by difference. Good results were obtained for alloys which contained only small amounts of elements other than copper and zinc. The results were less satisfactory for alloys containing considerable amounts of elements whose hydroxides were precipitated with ammonia, because these hydroxide precipitates held appreciable amounts of coprecipitated copper and zinc. The original paper should be consulted for further details.

4.8 Ferrocyanide. Ferrocyanide has been determined by spectrophotometric titration with standard 0·01 M cobalt (III) sulphate solution[12]. The method is identical to that used in section 4.12 (Bricker and Loeffler). 0·8–1·6 mg of iron as ferrocyanide were determined satisfactorily, but large amounts of ferrocyanide could not be titrated because of the limited solubility of cobalt (II) ferricyanide.

4.9 Gold. Hirano[81] has determined gold (III) as chloride by photometric titration with standard stannous chloride solution. For a satisfactory titration the acidity of the solution had to be less than 0·05 N and it was necessary to have an excess of chlorine water present to keep the gold in the trivalent state before the titration was started. The gold (III) was reduced to a purple colloidal solution of metallic gold. Presumably the reduction only occurred when all of the hypochlorous acid (chlorine water) had itself been reduced. There was no interference from copper, lead and small amounts of iron.

Gold (III) has also been titrated photometrically with standard potassium iodide solution[82].

4.10 Hydrazine. Bapat and Tatwawadi[75] have stated that hydrazine in sodium hydroxide solution may be satisfactorily titrated with standard potassium ferricyanide solution at about 460 mμ. Excess of ferricyanide ions absorb appreciably at this wavelength. However no further details were given.

4.11 Hypobromite. Hypobromite has been determined in solutions of pH 8–8·5 (bicarbonate buffer) by photometric titration at 430 mμ with standard 0·01 M potassium ferrocyanide solution[83]. The hypobromite was reduced to bromide and the ferrocyanide oxidized to ferricyanide. A plot of optical density against volume of titrant added consisted of a straight line of steep gradient to the end-point owing to the absorption of the ferricyanide ions formed during the titration, followed by an almost horizontal straight line after the end-point, because ferrocyanide ions in low concentrations scarcely absorb at 430 mμ. 0·4–2·4 mg of hypobromite were determined with a maximum error of 25 μg.

4.12 Iron. Iron (II) in sulphuric acid solution has been titrated quantitatively with spectrophotometric end-point detection using standard ceric sulphate solution[15]. At 360 mμ, cerium (IV) absorbs strongly and iron (III) slightly, so that the plot of optical density against volume of titrant added consists of a line of low gradient up to the end-point followed by a line of steep gradient after the end-point when the solution contains an excess of cerium (IV). The method was essentially developed for the determination of iron (III), which was reduced to iron (II) by passage through a 90% cadmium amalgam reductor before the titration. 0·3 to 3·5 mg amounts of iron were determined with an average error of 3 parts per thousand. These workers also determined mixtures of iron (II) and uranium (IV) by a similar method. That procedure will be discussed in section 4.15 under "uranium".

Procedure for iron alone. Pass a suitable aliquot of solution, 2 N in sulphuric acid and containing 0·3–3·5 mg of iron as iron (III) sulphate, through a cadmium amalgam reductor (0·5 cm in diameter, 20 cm in length) at about 4 ml/min and wash with 30 ml of 2 N acid, passing the last 20 ml through at a greatly increased rate. Collect the reduced solution in a suitable titration cell which has been de-aerated with nitrogen. Dilute the resulting solution with distilled water to about 90 ml and keep an atmosphere of nitrogen over the solution at all times. Set the wavelength to 360 mμ, start the stirrer and set the optical density reading to zero. Titrate the solution with 0·01 M ceric sulphate solution taking optical density readings after the additions of suitable increments of titrant. Locate the end-point graphically in the usual way.

Bricker and Loeffler[12] have determined iron (II) in sulphuric acid solution by spectrophotometric titration at 360 mμ with standard cobalt (III) sulphate solution. The course of the titration was followed from the steadily increasing optical density readings up to the end-point, as the concentration of iron (III) in the solution rose. At 360 mμ iron (III) absorbs appreciably. After the end-point the optical density readings increase only slowly because at this wavelength the excess of cobalt (III) sulphate absorbs only slightly. Iron (II) and cobalt (II) scarcely absorb at 360 mμ.

However the precision and accuracy of the method were not really satisfactory, 1–1·8 mg amounts of iron in about 90 ml of 6 N sulphuric acid being determined with a maximum error of 4%. The recoveries were high. In these titrations the burette was not emptied and filled with fresh cobalt (III) sulphate solution between determinations. Fresh solution was added to the burette as it was required. By working in this way, it was very probable that oxidation of water by the cobalt (III) sulphate was not negligible because some of the solution must have stood in the burette for as long as 30 minutes at room temperature (see 4.4—Bricker and Loeffler). This would explain the high results. Emptying and filling the burette between each determination would appear to be essential. It would also be an advantage to perform the spectrophotometric titrations at 0°C.

The cobalt (III) sulphate solution itself was standardized in a similar way against standard ferrous ammonium sulphate solution.

4.13 Selenite. Bapat and Tatwawadi[75] have determined selenite in sodium hydroxide solution by photometric titration at about 460 mμ, with standard potassium ferricyanide solution. The selenite is oxidized to selenate. A plot of optical density against volume of titrant added consists of a horizontal straight line to the end-point, followed by a line of steep gradient after the end-point, because ferricyanide ions in excess absorb appreciably at 460 mμ.

4.14 Thiosulphate. Thiosulphate in alkaline solution has been determined by photometric titration with standard potassium ferricyanide solution at about 460 mμ, but very few details of this method have been given[75]. The thiosulphate is oxidized to sulphate and the ferricyanide reduced to ferrocyanide. Only the ferricyanide in excess absorbs appreciably at 460 mμ.

4.15 Uranium. Bricker and Sweetser[15] have determined uranium (IV) by spectrophotometric titration at 360 mμ with standard ceric sulphate solution. Only cerium (IV) absorbs appreciably during the titration, hence the plot of optical density against volume of titrant added consists of a horizontal straight line to the end-point, followed by a line of steep gradient as an excess of cerium (IV) is added to the solution. The method was primarily developed for the determination of uranium (VI) after it had been reduced to uranium (IV), by passage of the solution through a 90% cadmium amalgam reductor. 0·6–9 mg amounts of uranium were determined with an average error of 3·4 parts per 1000.

Procedure. Pass a suitable aliquot of solution, 2 N in sulphuric acid and containing 0·6–9 mg of uranium as uranium (VI) sulphate, through a cadmium amalgam reductor (0·5 cm in diameter, 20 cm in length) at about 4 ml/min and wash with 30 ml of 2 N acid, passing the last 20 ml through at a greatly increased rate. Collect the reduced solution in a suitable titration cell which has been de-aerated with nitrogen. Dilute the resulting solution with distilled water to about 90 ml and keep an atmosphere of nitrogen over the solution at all times. Set the wavelength to 360 mμ, start the stirrer and set the optical density reading to zero. Titrate the solution with 0·01 M ceric sulphate solution in the usual way. Locate the end-point from the plot of optical density against volume of titrant added.

By a similar procedure, mixtures of iron and uranium may be determined[15]. (See 4.12—Bricker and Sweetser, for the determination of iron alone.) Iron (III) and uranium (VI) were reduced to iron (II) and uranium (IV) by passage through a cadmium amalgam reductor. In the spectrophotometric titration with standard ceric sulphate solution, the uranium (IV) was oxidized before the iron (II) and hence the determination of both elements was possible. In the uranium (IV) titration a wavelength of 345 mμ was employed, for it was necessary to locate the end-point using the increasing optical density readings after the end-point, as the concentration of iron (III) in the solution increased. Iron (III) absorbs more strongly at 345 mμ than at 360 mμ. However, to get a good end-point break in the iron (II) titration, the wavelength had to be increased to 360 mμ and the optical density reading readjusted to zero after sufficient readings had been obtained for the location of the uranium end-point.

Account must also be taken of the fact that a little iron (II) is oxidized along with the uranium (IV), and that the subsequent reaction between iron (III) and the last trace of uranium (IV) is slow. In addition the solution must be collected in an aliquot of ceric sulphate solution such that most of the uranium (IV) is immediately oxidized to uranium (VI). This is necessary in order to minimize the oxidation of uranium (IV) by oxygen dissolved in the solution, a reaction which is induced by ferrous ions. The original paper should be consulted for full details. Mixtures of 1–8 mg of uranium and

0·6–4 mg of iron were determined with average errors of about 6 parts per 1000 for the uranium and of about 8 parts per 1000 for the iron. 2·5–5 mg of uranium were determined satisfactorily in the presence of up to 25 times as much iron.

The method of Bricker and Sweetser[15], just described, has been modified by Menis *et al.*[48] in order to determine microgram quantities of uranium (IV). Titration plots of optical density against volume of titrant added were recorded automatically at 340 mμ. 12–240 μg amounts of uranium were determined with a coefficient of variation of 3%.

Procedure for manual titration. Transfer an aliquot of solution containing 12–240 μg of uranium (IV) to a titration cell in a suitable instrument and dilute to 35 ml with de-aerated 0·5 M sulphuric acid. Pass a stream of nitrogen over the surface of the liquid throughout the titration. Start the stirrer and set the wavelength to 340 mμ and the optical density reading to zero. Titrate the solution in the usual way with standard 0·001 N ceric sulphate solution. Locate the end-point from the plot of optical density against volume of titrant added.

4.16 Vanadium. Goddu and Hume[41] have applied spectrophotometric end-point detection to the determination of vanadium (IV) from steels by titration with standard permanganate solution. A photometric titration at 525 mμ was used in order to improve upon the visual titration, particularly in coloured solutions. The vanadium was obtained in the quadrivalent state by the ferrous sulphate–persulphate method[84]. At 525 mμ, only the excess of permanganate ion absorbs and so the plot of optical density against volume of titrant added consists of a horizontal straight line to the end-point, followed by a line of steep gradient after the end-point, owing to the strong absorption of the permanganate ion. Vanadium (IV) in concentrations as low as 5 μg/ml was determined with an accuracy and precision of 1%. With the exception of chromium and tungsten, there is no interference from the other elements commonly present in steels. Interference from tungsten is prevented by removing the tungsten as tungstic acid. Chromium only interferes if present in amounts greater than 10 times that of the vanadium. The method was applied with excellent results to the analysis of steels and ferro-titanium.

Procedure for steel (free from tungsten). Weigh a sample of steel containing 5–15 mg of vanadium into a 150 ml beaker and add 10 ml of water and 12 ml of 60% perchloric acid solution. Heat on a hot plate until the steel has dissolved. Boil the solution over a low flame until the fuming perchloric acid has oxidized the chromium and manganese to chromium (VI) and manganese (VII) respectively. Cool the solution and dilute to 80 ml. Transfer the solution to a suitable titration cell, rinse the beaker with a little 0·5% perchloric acid and add 3 ml of 85% phosphoric acid. Add 0·1 N ferrous sulphate solution (in 0·5% perchloric acid) until a slight excess is present as shown by a spot test of a drop of the solution with ferricyanide. Then add 5 ml of the ferrous sulphate solution in excess.

Start the stirrer into motion, set the wavelength to 525 mμ and the optical density reading to zero, and add 2·5 ml of ammonium persulphate solution (15% w/v). After 1 min titrate the solution with 0·1 N permanganate solution, adding the titrant in suitable increments. Plot the optical density readings against the volume of titrant added, and extrapolate the line beyond the end-point downwards to the horizontal baseline to obtain the true end-point.

Notes. (1) With tungsten steels the method is similar, but the tungstic acid must be removed from the solution by filtration after fuming with perchloric acid.

(2) Miles and Englis[79] have stated that vanadium (V) may be determined by spectrophotometric titration at 350 mμ with standard ferrous sulphate solution. They do not, however, give any results for the determination of vanadium (V) alone in solution, by this method. They were primarily interested in the determination of both chromium (VI) and vanadium (V) in solution. The spectrophotometric titration of mixtures of these elements has already been discussed in section 4.5.

(3) Vanadium in ferro-vanadium and steel has also been determined by Barkovskii[85], using a photometric titration of the vanadium in the pentavalent state with standard ferrous ammonium sulphate solution.

(4) Tatwawadi[86] has determined the concentration of a vanadium (IV) sulphate solution by using the solution to titrate photometrically a suitable aliquot of standard potassium ferricyanide solution. The ferricyanide is reduced to ferrocyanide and the vanadium (IV) oxidized to vanadium (V). Titrations were performed at about 470 mμ where only the ferricyanide ion absorbs strongly. Hence the optical density readings decreased steadily to the end-point and then remained constant after the end-point. By this method, vanadium was accurately determined in solutions containing about 2–6 mg of the metal per ml.

4.17 Tannins. In the determination of tannins using the Löwenthal method[87] where an aliquot of tannin solution is titrated with standard permanganate in the presence of indigo carmine as indicator, the colour change at the end-point is from green to yellow. However, a visual titration is difficult and Zitko[88] has applied photometric end-point detection to this titration. The end-point is readily located at the intersection of two lines on the plot of optical density against volume of titrant added.

CHAPTER 5

COMPLEXOMETRIC TITRATIONS

5.1 In the vast majority of these titrations, EDTA (ethylenediaminetetra-acetate) has been employed as titrant. A great many papers appear each year on the application of EDTA to titrimetric determinations, and it is logical that photometric end-point detection should be employed for systems where the visual end-point is difficult, either because a considerable portion of metal ions is bound as a metal-indicator complex at the beginning of the titration, or because traces of impurity, complexing very strongly with the indicator, are producing a drawn-out visual end-point.

Where EDTA is the titrant, no mention will be made of the particular salt used for any one titration. In most cases, a standard solution of the disodium salt of EDTA has been employed. The dihydrate of the disodium salt is readily obtained in the pure state and, after drying at 80°C, this salt may be used as a primary standard. A saturated solution of the disodium salt at room temperature is about 0·3 M and has a pH of 4·7. When titrations are carried out in buffered solutions, a standard solution of the disodium salt is, in all cases, satisfactory as the titrant. However, when titrations are performed in unbuffered solutions, as is sometimes desirable, it may be better to employ standard solutions of the free acid or of the tetrasodium salt, depending on the pH of the solution to which the titrant is to be added. For titrations in unbuffered acidic solutions, the free acid can be used as titrant, but it has only a limited solubility in water and a saturated solution at room temperature is about 0·007 M with a pH of about 2·3. With titrations in unbuffered alkaline solutions, the use of the disodium salt may cause the pH of the solution to fall more than is desirable, because of the hydrogen ions released during the formation of the metal–EDTA complex. It is then better to employ a standard solution of the tetrasodium salt. This salt is much more soluble than the free acid and disodium salt and it forms a 60 per cent solution at room temperature with a pH of 10·6.

For those who may not have had much experience of EDTA and other complexans as titrants, two excellent articles by Reilley *et al.*[89, 90] have recently appeared on the use of these reagents. In these articles, useful information is given about the less obvious factors which can affect the quality of the end-point, such as the concentrations of buffering reagents.

5.2 Barium. The photometric titration of pure barium solutions with EDTA presents no difficulties. For the determination of 0·1–5 mg of barium, Rowley and co-workers[91] adapted the method of Manns *et al.*[92] who titrated 500 mg of barium visually with EDTA using eriochrome black T as indicator. The titrations were carried out in a cell which fitted into a Coleman Universal spectrophotometer; a wavelength of 650 mμ was used. 0·002 or 0·01 M EDTA was employed as titrant depending on the quantity of barium being titrated, and magnesium ions, which must be added to the system if a colour change is to occur, were present in the titrant. During the titration, free barium ions are first complexed and then the titrant removes the magnesium from the magnesium–indicator complex. The colour changes from wine red to blue during the process. (Barium does not form a stable complex with eriochrome black T.) The solution was buffered at pH 10 with ammonia–ammonium chloride. The end-point was located from a plot of optical density against volume of titrant added. The precision and accuracy of the method were good, the maximum error for 0·1–1 mg of barium being $\pm$ 0·02 mg.

Cohen and Gordon[93] have also titrated 0·05–12 mg of barium with EDTA using *o*-cresolphthalein complexan as indicator in a solution buffered at pH 11. They state that the end-points are sharper with this indicator than by the above method of Rowley *et al.*[91] where eriochrome black T was employed. The maximum error for 0·05–2 mg of barium was $\pm$ 0·01 mg and for 2–12 mg $\pm$ 0·04 mg.

Procedure. Add to a suitable titration cell a sample for analysis which contains 0·05 to 12 mg of barium in 1–5 ml of neutral, carbonate-free solution. Add 10 ml of ammonia–ammonium chloride buffer solution and dilute to about 60 ml. Place the titration cell in a filter photometer or spectrophotometer and select a wavelength of 570 mμ. Adjust the instrument so that the optical density of the solution is zero. Add 10 drops of *o*-cresolphthalein complexan solution (0·1 % w/v in triethanolamine). Set the stirrer in motion and titrate with 0·01 M EDTA if more than 2 mg of barium is present and with 0·002 M EDTA if less is present. Near the end-point take 0·050 ml and 0·100 ml increments for 0·01 M and 0·002 M EDTA solutions, respectively. Allow the solution to mix for 1–2 min before measuring the optical density. Determine the end-point from the usual plot. Determine the blank correction (to be subtracted) by a similar titration in the absence of barium.

While these methods are completely satisfactory for the titration of barium alone in solution or associated only with alkali metals, they are obviously inapplicable in the presence of unknown amounts of magnesium, other alkaline earths, and many other metal ions. Initial separation is therefore essential if barium in such solutions is to be determined by photometric titration with EDTA.

Headridge and Magee[39] have shown that a spectrophotometric titration can be applied to the determination of barium, after its separation from other Group II elements by paper chromatography. The barium after removal from the chromatographic paper was titrated with EDTA using eriochrome black T as indicator by a method similar to that of Rowley *et al.*[91]. Minute traces of iron and other metallic impurities removed from the paper along with the barium were complexed with cyanide.

The method was used to determine barium oxide in a 50 mg sample of barytocalcite and the authors stated that a 3 mg sample could be analysed, if a slight modification in the method was employed. The accuracy was ± 1 % of the total contents for amounts of oxide up to 20 %, and ± 2 % where the amount of oxide exceeded 20 %. Magnesium, calcium and strontium, if present in the sample, could be determined by the same procedure.

5.3 Bismuth. Underwood[94] has titrated bismuth spectrophotometrically with EDTA, using cupric nitrate as indicator for 5–100 mg amounts in 100 ml of solution, and thiourea for 0·5–10 mg quantities in the same volume of solution. Bismuth forms a more stable complex than copper with EDTA and, after the end-point in the bismuth titration, the optical density of the solution rises steadily if measurements are made at 745 mμ where the copper (II)–EDTA complex, but not the bismuth–EDTA complex, absorbs. Thiourea forms a yellow complex with bismuth, but this is broken down on the addition of EDTA with the formation of the more stable bismuth–EDTA complex. Hence the optical density readings fall steadily to the end-point, if measurements are made at 400 mμ where the bismuth–thiourea complex absorbs. The maximum errors in the determination of pure bismuth solutions were 9 and 14 parts in 1000, with cupric nitrate and thiourea respectively.

The interferences of tin, lead, copper and iron were investigated. Iron and tin interfere when either indicator is used. Obviously copper will not interfere when cupric nitrate is the indicator but with thiourea, 5 mg or more of copper interfere by forming a precipitate with the indicator. Lead only interferes in large quantities. The maximum amounts permitted are 1 g with thiourea and 3 g with cupric nitrate. If the sample solution contains tin, it is readily removed along with arsenic and antimony before the titration by adding hydrobromic acid and bromine to the solution, and fuming with perchloric acid.

Procedure. With cupric nitrate—To a bismuth solution containing from 5 to 100 mg of bismuth, add 2 g of solid chloroacetic acid and 1 ml of 1 M cupric nitrate solution. Adjust the volume of the solution to about 100 ml and its pH to about 2 using 1 : 1 ammonia or 5 M sodium hydroxide. Transfer the solution to the titration cell of a suitable spectrophotometer and set the instrument to zero optical density at 745 mμ. Titrate with 0·1 M EDTA solution. Read the optical density after additions of appropriate increments of titrant, obtaining as many points as desired to define the two straight lines whose intersection gives the end-point.

With thiourea—To the bismuth solution, containing 0·5–10 mg of bismuth, add 0·5 g of solid chloroacetic acid and dilute the solution to 100 ml. Adjust the pH to a value of about 2, using 1 : 1 ammonia or 5 M sodium hydroxide solution. Heat the solution to about 70°C, holding it at this temperature for 10–15 min. Cool the solution to room temperature and transfer it to the titration cell. Adjust the controls to obtain zero optical density. Then add 5 ml of a 1 M aqueous solution of thiourea. The optical density will increase immediately to its maximum value, after which the titration may be started with 0·01 M EDTA solution.

Notes. (1) Wilhite and Underwood[95] have also titrated spectrophotometrically with EDTA, 0·2–6 mg of bismuth in 100 ml of solution at 265 mμ, the method depending on the fact that the bismuth–EDTA complex absorbs strongly at 265 mμ while bismuth does not absorb at that wavelength. However, the determinations are not as accurate as those just mentioned where cupric nitrate or thiourea are used as indicators. Without an indicator present the maximum error was 55 parts in 1000. The method may, however, have its uses since lead, cadmium, zinc, cobalt and nickel ions do not interfere with the determination of bismuth. In addition bismuth and lead may be determined simultaneously (see under lead, section 5.9).

(2) Milligram amounts of bismuth in solutions of pH 1 to 5 have also been titrated quantitatively with photometric end-point detection with EDTA using potassium iodide as indicator[96]. A photometer was adapted for the titrations and a filter with maximum transmission in the region of 450 mμ was used. As the titration proceeded, the optical density of the solution decreased steadily as the bismuth–iodide complex was broken down on the formation of the more

stable bismuth–EDTA complex. The end-point occurred at the intersection of straight lines on the usual plot of optical density against volume of titrant added. Chloride, fluoride, tartrate and oxalate interfere in the titration.

Bismuth has been determined by photometric titration with standard EDTA using pyrocatechol violet as indicator[97]. Because the pH of the bismuth solution was 2–3, no interference resulted from the presence of aluminium and the majority of univalent and divalent ions. Interference from iron (III) could be prevented by reduction to iron (II) with ascorbic acid. 0·2–25 mg of bismuth were determined with an error not exceeding 0·01 mg and 25–140 mg with a maximum error of 0·7 mg.

Procedure. Add an aliquot of bismuth solution, as nitrate, to a suitable cell for a photometric titration and dilute the solution with distilled water to 70–100 ml. Add 3–4 drops of indicator solution (0·1 % aqueous) and ammonium hydroxide solution until the pH is in the range of 2–3. Place a yellow filter in the instrument, start the stirrer into motion and adjust the optical density reading to a high value. The colour of the solution changes from blue to golden yellow in the vicinity of the end-point. Titrate the solution with 0·001–0·1 M EDTA solution, depending on the approximate amount of bismuth to be expected, and record optical density readings after the addition of suitable volumes of titrant. Locate the end-point graphically.

5.4 Cadmium. Sweetser and Bricker[98] determined cadmium in solution buffered at pH 10 with ammonia and ammonium chloride by spectrophotometric titration with EDTA at 222–228 mμ. The method was the same as that used by these workers for the spectrophotometric titration of calcium and magnesium (5(b)). Using a 0·001 M solution of EDTA, 1 mg amounts of cadmium were determined with an accuracy of $\pm$ 0·7 %, while with 0·01 M EDTA, 10 mg amounts were determined to within $\pm$ 0·4 %.

Cadmium was also determined in the presence of zinc by titrating with 0·013 M EDTA at 236 mμ, a solution 0·6 N with respect to sodium hydroxide and containing a low concentration of cyanide ions. In strongly alkaline solution the zincate ion is not complexed by EDTA. The cyanide was present in order to keep the cadmium in solution. By that method 11 mg of cadmium were determined satisfactorily in the presence of 3–50 mg of zinc. The maximum error was 0·4 %.

5.5 Calcium and magnesium. The first photometric titrations of any of the Group II elements were made independently by a number of workers in 1952 and 1953 who used the technique to determine calcium in serum. Interest in this method was stimulated by the fact that visual EDTA titrations of small volumes (0·1–0·2 ml) of serum for calcium, using murexide as indicator, are difficult because of the gradual colour change in the vicinity of the equivalence point. In addition, certain serums have a high bilirubin content and very little change in colour intensity can be observed visually throughout the titration. That better results were obtained by photometric titration was shown by Kibrick *et al.*[99], Fales[100] and Lehmann[101]. At about this time Chalmers[102] also reported his findings on the photometric titration of microgram quantities of calcium in pure solutions, and in the presence of magnesium.

Over 30 papers have appeared on the photometric titration of calcium and/or magnesium, and the papers in this section have been arranged under the following headings—biological materials, synthetic solutions, rocks and minerals, water and alloys.

(a) *Biological materials.* Kibrick *et al.*[99] used a photometric titration with EDTA at 580 mμ, with murexide as indicator, for the determination of calcium in serum. The solution was buffered at pH 11·6 (boric acid–sodium hydroxide). Small amounts of magnesium in the serum were not titrated because magnesium is precipitated as hydroxide above pH about 11. Titrations were performed on solutions from which protein had been precipitated with picric acid, and also in the presence of protein. In this latter case, 0·2 ml of serum was employed and the results deviated between −0·5 and +0·3 mg of calcium/100 ml from values obtained by the standard oxalate–permanganate method.

Fales[100] determined calcium in 0·1 ml of serum (micro-method) or 1·0 ml (macro-method) by titrating spectrophotometrically at 620 mμ with standard EDTA solution. The results were in good agreement with those obtained by the Clark–Collip method[103] (an oxalate–permanganate method).

Procedure for micro amounts. Add 10 ml of distilled water, 0·2 ml of 9 N sodium hydroxide and 2 drops of murexide solution to a test tube. Mix the solution and pipette 1 ml quantities into each of three titration cells. To two of the cells, add 0·1 ml of serum. The solution in the third cell serves as a blank. Add 0·2 ml of standard EDTA solution (0·0005 M) to the blank and 0·1 ml to the duplicate test solutions. After mixing, place the blank titration cell in a suitable spectrophotometer and adjust the optical density reading to say 0·3, with the wavelength scale at 620 mμ. Then measure the optical densities of each of the test solutions. Add

0·1 ml of titrant to each cell, again adjust the optical density to 0·3 for the blank and read the optical densities of the test solutions. Carry on in this manner until the optical densities of the test solutions, after rising, are steady. Then plot optical density against volume of titrant added for each test solution, and from the graphs determine the end-points in the usual manner. Average the end-point titres for the test solutions.

Note. The method of balancing with a blank was employed by Fales to counteract any errors that might be caused by dilution or by any fading of the murexide indicator which may occur in these titrations.

Procedure for macro amounts. To suitable titration cells add 9 ml of water, 1 ml of serum, 0·2 ml of 9 N sodium hydroxide solution and 2 drops of murexide solution. To the third cell, serving as a blank, add 10 ml of distilled water, 0·2 ml of 9 N sodium hydroxide solution and 2 drops of indicator solution. Carry out the titration as in the micro-method but add 1 ml increments of titrant.

Notes. (1) Lehmann[101] also determined calcium in serum by photometric and spectrophotometric titration with 0·001 M EDTA using murexide at 505 mμ in a solution of pH about 13 (sodium hydroxide). The results were about 0·4 mg of calcium/100 ml lower than those obtained by the Kramer and Tisdall method[104] (an oxalate–permanganate method).

(2) Serum calcium has also been determined by spectrophotometric titration at 600 mμ with EDTA (about 0·0005 M), using murexide as indicator in a solution of pH about 13·2[105]. The method was a simplification of the method of Fales[100] and a series of results obtained by this method were compared with results obtained using the Clark–Collip method[103]. It was found that the EDTA method gave on average lower values than those obtained by the Clark–Collip method, and the best agreement was obtained when the EDTA values were multiplied by 1·046.

A further application of photometric end-point detection to the determination of calcium in biological materials by titration with EDTA using murexide as indicator was made by Horner[106]. Magnesium and iron in the concentrations usually present in such materials caused no interference. The results compared very favourably with those obtained by the standard oxalate–permanganate method for calcium.

Procedure for serum. To a suitable cell for a filter photometer or spectrophotometer add 1 ml of serum, 1 ml of 1·5 N sodium hydroxide solution and 2 ml of murexide solution (0·018% (w/v) freshly prepared). Set the stirrer in motion, and adjust the wavelength to 620 mμ and the optical density reading to zero. Titrate the solution with 0·0005 M EDTA solution adding the titrant in 1 ml increments and taking optical density readings after each addition of titrant. Determine the end-point from a plot of optical density against volume of titrant added.

Procedure for urine or ashed biological specimens. Pipette 4 ml of sample solution into a 15 ml centrifuge tube. Add 2 ml of tungstate reagent (66% (w/v) of $Na_2WO_4{\cdot}2H_2O$) and 4 ml of morpholine nitrate–nitric acid reagent (equal portions of morpholine nitrate, 48% (w/v), and

4 N nitric acid solutions, mixed) and mix well. An immediate precipitate of both phosphotungstate and morpholine tungstate will be noted. Allow the tube to stand for 1 hr to ensure complete precipitation. Centrifuge for several minutes. Pipette 1 ml of the clear supernatant liquid into the titration cell, add 1 ml of 1·5 N sodium hydroxide solution and 2 ml of murexide solution, and carry on as before.

Notes. (1) Serums having phosphate concentrations exceeding 10 mg/100 ml should also be freed of phosphate before titration.

(2) Errors due to dilution effects are prevented when the titrant contains the same concentration of indicator as the solution being titrated.

Kenny and Toverud[107] have also applied the photometric titration method of Fales[100] to the determination of calcium in serum containing a considerable concentration of phosphate. Phosphate does not interfere in the calcium determinations at least up to a phosphate to calcium ratio of 8 : 1 by weight.

Again, a similar method has been employed by Poulie[108] for the titration of 0·5 ml samples of serum. Titrations were carried out at 600 mμ. The method may also be used for the determination of calcium in urine, if the urine is suitably diluted to prevent interference from phosphate and oxalate.

Zak *et al.*[109] also used the technique of photometric titration to determine serum calcium. Again EDTA was used as titrant and murexide as indicator. These workers also determined the total calcium and magnesium in serum by titrating spectrophotometrically at 660 mμ, a solution buffered to pH 10, with EDTA using eriochrome black T as indicator. The magnesium in serum was obtained by subtraction. Phosphate in concentrations usually present in serum did not interfere in the methods.

Wilkinson[110] also employed a photometric EDTA titration at 575 mμ for the determination of calcium in 0·1 ml volumes of serum. Murexide was again employed as indicator in a solution of pH 12·6. The method was very similar to those already described. The accuracy was $\pm$ 0·1 mg per 100 ml in the range 1–40 mg of calcium per 100 ml in synthetic solutions with or without magnesium being present. For serums, the method gave results 0·7–0·8 mg of calcium per 100 ml lower than an oxalate precipitation method, but Wilkinson was of the opinion that the murexide figures represented the true calcium content.

Wilkinson also determined the sum of calcium and magnesium in 0·1 ml of serum by titrating photometrically with standard EDTA solution at 600 mμ, the peak transmission for the filter which was employed. The solution contained eriochrome black T as indicator and was buffered to pH 10·4 with ethanolamine. The magnesium in serum was obtained by subtraction. For synthetic solutions the accuracy of the determinations was $\pm$ 0·1 mg per 100 ml for 0·2–10 mg per 100 ml of magnesium.

A method very similar to that used by Wilkinson[110] was employed by Claes *et al.*[111] for the routine determination of serum magnesium.

Zak *et al.*[112] determined calcium and magnesium in spinal fluid by spectrophotometric titration with EDTA at 660 mμ. Both elements were determined in the presence of eriochrome black T after an initial separation from each other. The EDTA solution also contained magnesium–EDTA complex so that the calcium could be satisfactorily titrated with eriochrome black T as indicator. (Calcium does not form a stable complex with eriochrome black T.) The calcium was precipitated from 2 ml of spinal fluid as oxalate, the precipitate was centrifuged down and magnesium determined in a suitable aliquot of the centrifugate.

The precipitate of calcium oxalate was washed and fumed with perchloric acid to destroy oxalate. The resulting calcium perchlorate solution was titrated with EDTA. The results were satisfactory. Calcium in spinal fluid (9·7–14·4 mg/100 ml) was determined with a maximum error of 0·8 mg/100 ml and magnesium (5·3–9·8 mg/100 ml) with a maximum error of 0·3 mg/100 ml. Phosphate in the concentrations usually present in spinal fluid did not interfere in the method.

Calcium and magnesium in 0·1 ml of serum have also been titrated quantitatively with EDTA by Robinson and Rathbun[113] using spectrophotometric end-point detection and only one indicator, eriochrome black T. The sum of calcium and magnesium was determined in a titration at 660 mμ employing a solution buffered at pH 10·4 with ethanolamine. For the determination of magnesium, 0·1 ml of serum and 0·1 ml of 2% (w/v) ammonium oxalate solution were shaken to precipitate the calcium as oxalate. The precipitate was centrifuged down and 0·1 ml of the centrifugate were titrated spectrophotometrically with EDTA solution as for the sum of calcium and magnesium. The results were satisfactory.

Malmstadt and Hadjiioannou[114] have determined calcium and magnesium in deproteinized blood serum by automatic photometric titration with standard EDTA solution at 650 mμ. The Sargent–Malmstadt spectro-electro derivative titrator (2.6) was employed.

Total calcium and magnesium were determined using eriochrome black T as indicator at pH about 10 while calcium alone was titrated in a solution of pH about 13 (sodium hydroxide) using calcon (C.I. Mordant Black 17) as indicator. A sample of serum was analysed for calcium and magnesium in 5 min. The results for calcium were of the same degree of accuracy and reproducibility as those obtained by the classical permanganate titration of precipitated calcium oxalate[103].

The method of Ramaiah and Vishnu[122] (5.5(b)) was adapted by Ramaiah, Vishnu and Chaturvedi[115] to the determination of calcium in sugar house products. The diluted molasses solution (10 Bx) was clarified with dry lead subacetate and filtered. The excess of lead in the filtrate, along with other interfering ions, was precipitated with potassium ferrocyanide. The calcium in the filtrate was titrated at 630 mμ with EDTA solution using copper (II)–ammonia complex as indicator. Concentrations of calcium oxide in the range 1·3–2·2% per 100 Bx of molasses were satisfactorily determined.

Plant materials have been analysed for calcium and magnesium by making use of automatic derivative photometric titrations with standard EDTA solution[116]. One gram samples of dried material were treated with concentrated nitric acid and 70% (w/w) perchloric acid to oxidize the organic material. The inorganic salts were finally obtained in 50 ml of solution, 0·5 N with respect to hydrochloric acid. Phosphate was precipitated as zirconium phosphate from a 10 ml aliquot of solution and removed by centrifugation. The heavy metals were removed from the centrifugate by extraction of their diethyldithiocarbamates into carbon tetrachloride. The aqueous solution was then diluted to 25 ml in a graduated flask.

The sum of calcium and magnesium was determined in a 10 ml aliquot of the solution buffered with ammonium hydroxide and ammonium chloride, and containing triethanolamine to mask remaining traces of iron, manganese, copper and aluminium, which might otherwise block the indicator. The titrant was 0·01 M EDTA and the indicator eriochrome black T.

The calcium alone was determined in 10 ml of the solution, containing triethanolamine, and adjusted to pH 13 by the addition of sodium hydroxide solution. The titrant was again EDTA and the indicator calcon (C.I. Mordant Black 17). In both titrations, the end-points were determined automatically using the Sargent–Malmstadt spectro-electro titrator (2.6) and a wavelength of 650 mμ.

Calcium and magnesium in plant materials containing 1–4% of calcium and 0·2–1% of magnesium were generally determined to within $\pm$0·03% of the total contents.

Some of the facts just presented in this sub-section on the determination of calcium and magnesium in biological materials warrant further discussion. In addition it is as well to examine these titrations in the light of recent developments which have been made into the complexometric titration of calcium.

It will be obvious from the preceding paragraphs and from later references in this section that calcium has been titrated with EDTA in the presence of murexide as indicator at a number of different wavelengths. These fall into two groups, namely 505 or 510 mμ and 575–620 mμ. Schwarzenbach[117] has plotted molar extinction coefficient against wavelength for free murexide and the calcium–murexide complex at pH 13 and a difference spectrum constructed from these curves shows that the greatest difference in molar extinction coefficients occurs at 505 mμ ($\epsilon_{\text{Ca murexide}} - \epsilon_{\text{murexide}} = 9900$). Hence the use of wavelengths of 505 and 510 mμ. However, at 505 mμ the calcium–murexide complex absorbs more strongly than the free indicator, and therefore in the titration of calcium with EDTA, the optical density readings fall as the end-point is approached, with the result that a preliminary titration is usually necessary to find the best setting of the relative optical density reading at the start of the titration. It is therefore more convenient to work near the wavelength at which there is the greatest increase in relative optical density in the vicinity of the end-point, for now the relative optical density can be set to zero at the beginning of the titration. The greatest increase occurs at 580 mμ ($\epsilon_{\text{murexide}} - \epsilon_{\text{Ca murexide}} = 8100$). As the wavelength increases above 580 mμ the magnitude of the change in relative optical density during the titration decreases, but at 620 mμ a satisfactory spectrophotometric titration may still be made for then $\epsilon_{\text{murexide}} - \epsilon_{\text{Ca murexide}}$ has still the high value of 5300.

A similar treatment of the absorption spectra for free eriochrome black T and the magnesium–eriochrome black T complex[118] shows that the optimum wavelengths for spectrophotometric titration are 630 mμ (for rising optical density readings during the titration) and 530 mμ (for falling optical density readings). However, titrations are satisfactory anywhere in the regions of 620–675 mμ and 510–550 mμ.

It also appears that calcon (C.I. Mordant Black 17) is a better indicator than murexide for the EDTA titration of calcium in the presence of magnesium. Belcher *et al.*[119] have made a study of these titrations using various indicators. They concluded that for pure calcium solution, or for conditions where the magnesium : calcium ratio is $< 1 : 12$, acid alizarin black SN (C.I. Mordant Black 25) is the best indicator, whereas for higher magnesium ratios, calcon is the only reliable indicator. Their original paper should be consulted for details.

When the results for the determination of calcium in serum using (a) an oxalate–permanganate method, and (b) the EDTA–murexide method, are compared it is evident that good agreement between the results for both methods was obtained by some workers, e.g. Fales[100] and Horner[106] while others found that the EDTA–murexide method produced lower results than an oxalate–permanganate method, e.g. Lehmann[101], Eldjarn[105] and Wilkinson[110]. The reason for these discrepancies is not obvious. Since the EDTA–murexide methods are all very similar, it is possible that the differences arise because of variations in the oxalate–permanganate methods. In a recent paper, Bett and Fraser[120] have developed a rapid micro-method for determining serum calcium using the disappearance of the fluorescence of the calcium–calcein complex when calcium is titrated with EDTA in the presence of this indicator. These workers compared the results of their method with those obtained by the EDTA–murexide method (a modification of the method of Kibrick[99]) and the Kramer–Tisdall method[104] (an oxalate–permanganate method). They were all in good agreement. For example, the mean results for 30 sera analysed by the three techniques are shown in Table 1. It is evident from these results that there are no significant differences between the three methods and it is therefore reasonable to conclude that the EDTA–murexide method is reliable and does indeed produce the correct result.

There is now a possibility that the photometric titration methods for calcium in serum using EDTA as titrant and murexide or calcon as indicator may be superseded by a fluorimetric titration procedure in which the calcium in sodium hydroxide solution (pH about 13) is titrated in a cell with EDTA solution using calcein (fluorescein complexan) as indicator[120]. The contents of the cell are illuminated by ultra-violet light and the end-point is reached when the fluorescence of the solution disappears. The calcium–indicator complex fluoresces strongly but the free indicator does not. This method is more convenient than a photometric titration and the results are comparable with those obtained by the EDTA–murexide and Kramer–Tisdall methods (see Table 1). Bett and Fraser[120] also state that 0·5 μg of calcium in 3 ml of solution may be determined successfully. With the murexide titration the method is most sensitive at 505 mμ (see above), where $\epsilon_{\text{Ca murexide}} - \epsilon_{\text{murexide}} =$ 9900. Now if it is assumed that the minimum optical density change required for a satisfactory titration using the normal method of spectrophotometric end-point detection is 0·1 units, it is readily

TABLE 1

Method	Mean (*mg/100 ml*) + S.D.
Ultra-violet titration (fluorescence method)	9·46 ± 0·23
Kramer–Tisdall	9·38 ± 0·38
EDTA–murexide	9·49 ± 0·36

calculated that this lower limit of sensitivity is achieved with 1·2 μg of calcium/3 ml of solution in a 1 cm cell. The ultra-violet titration method is therefore not only more convenient but also more sensitive than the murexide titration method.

(b) *Synthetic solutions.* Sweetser and Bricker[98] were able to determine calcium or magnesium, and calcium in the presence of magnesium, by spectrophotometric titration with EDTA solution without the use of an added indicator. The titrations were carried out at 222–236 mμ. The method was possible because above pH 7 the calcium and magnesium complexes of EDTA absorb less strongly than EDTA itself in the ultra-violet region of the spectrum indicated above.

With 0·001 M EDTA as titrant, 200–400 μg of calcium and 80–200 μg of magnesium were determined separately in solutions at pH 10 (ammonia–ammonium chloride buffer) with errors of

$\pm$ 0·2% and $\pm$ 0·9% respectively. When 0·01 M EDTA was used, 2–4 mg of calcium and 2 mg of magnesium were similarly determined with errors of $\pm$ 0·25% and $\pm$ 0·3% respectively.

Titrations were performed at pH 13·8 (sodium hydroxide) in solutions containing citrate for the determination of calcium in the presence of magnesium. (Citrate forms a weak complex with calcium and helps to prevent the calcium from being coprecipitated on the magnesium hydroxide precipitate.) For 2–4 mg of calcium the recoveries were slightly low in the presence of magnesium, even with citrate present. The negative error increased steadily with increasing concentration of magnesium until, for weights of magnesium equal to the calcium taken, it was about −1·7%.

Procedure for calcium or magnesium. Pipette 5–50 ml of calcium or magnesium solution containing 200–400 μg of calcium or 80–200 μg of magnesium into a suitable titration cell for a spectrophotometer. Add 2 ml of ammonia–ammonium chloride buffer solution to give a pH of 10 and dilute to about 100 ml. Set the stirrer in motion and adjust the wavelength to 222 mμ. Set the optical density to zero and titrate with standard 0·001 M EDTA solution. Record optical density readings after each addition of titrant and determine the end-point from a plot of optical density against volume of titrant added.

Note. If milligram amounts of calcium and magnesium are to be titrated use 0·01 M EDTA and a wavelength of 228 mμ.

Ringbom and Vänninen[32] have titrated magnesium sulphate solution photometrically with standard EDTA solution using eriochrome black T as indicator. The solution was buffered at pH 10 with ammonia and ammonium chloride. They showed that amounts of magnesium around 5 mg could be determined by photometric titration with an accuracy of $\pm$ 0·2%.

In order to demonstrate that titration curves derived theoretically by Fortuin *et al.*[29] are in fact obtained in practice, Karsten and co-workers[118] titrated photometrically calcium with EDTA using murexide or *o*-cresolphthalein complexan as indicator, and magnesium with EDTA using eriochrome black T or *o*-cresolphthalein complexan.

In each case about 150 ml of solution containing about 20 mg of calcium or about 30 mg of magnesium were titrated. For calcium with murexide, the solution was adjusted to pH 12 with sodium hydroxide. For magnesium with eriochrome black T, and calcium and magnesium with *o*-cresolphthalein complexan, the solution was buffered to pH 10. For murexide, eriochrome black T and *o*-cresolphthalein complexan, wavelengths of 580 mμ, 546 mμ and 546 mμ were employed respectively. The accuracy of the determinations was ± 0·5% and the precision even better.

Chalmers[102] determined microgram quantities of calcium in pure solution and in the presence of magnesium by spectrophotometric titration with EDTA using murexide as indicator. 20–150 μg of calcium were determined with a maximum error of 2 μg.

Procedure. Transfer approximately 1 ml of the calcium solution, which should contain 10–200 μg of calcium, to a suitable cell for a spectrophotometric titration. Add 4–8 mg of murexide indicator powder (0·5% w/w in solid potassium sulphate), stir and add 2 N sodium hydroxide solution dropwise until a strong pink colour appears, and add a further 2–4 drops. Dilute the solution with water to about 3·5 ml. Place the titration cell in position and set the wavelength to 610 mμ and the optical density to zero. Titrate with 0·01 N EDTA from a syringe micro-burette, stirring the solution after each addition of titrant. Towards the end-point add the titrant in 0·005 ml increments. Obtain the end-point from a plot of optical density against volume of titrant added.

Note. Stengel and Riemer[121] have also reported on the photometric EDTA titration of calcium with murexide as indicator and of calcium plus magnesium with eriochrome black T.

Calcium in pure solution has been determined by a type of spectrophotometric titration with EDTA after the addition of copper (II) sulphate as indicator[122]. The method is based on the fact that, in strongly ammoniacal solution, the calcium–EDTA complex is formed in preference to the copper (II)–EDTA complex. If an ammoniacal solution containing calcium and copper (II) ions is therefore titrated with EDTA, all of the calcium is titrated before the EDTA starts to remove copper from the copper (II)–ammonia complex. The titration was made at 630 mμ where the copper (II)–ammonia complex absorbs strongly. The optical density remained at a steady high value until all of the calcium was titrated and then fell steadily as the copper (II)–ammonia complex was broken down by the excess of EDTA over calcium. The end-point occurred at the intersection of two straight lines on the plot of optical density against volume of titrant added.

Ramaiah and Vishnu did not carry out the titration in a cell fitted into a spectrophotometer, but added increasing amounts of EDTA solution to the same concentrations of calcium and copper (II) ions in 25 ml graduated flasks. The optical density of each solution was measured after making up to the mark with distilled water. The solutions were all 2 N with respect to ammonia.

Obviously it would be much better to titrate only one aliquot of the calcium solution in a suitable cell constructed to fit into the cell compartment of a spectrophotometer—to employ, in fact, the technique used for almost all spectrophotometric titrations.

10–60 mg of calcium were determined by the above method with an accuracy of $\pm 2\%$.

Riley[123] determined calcium and magnesium from synthetic mixtures of many elements by titrating photometrically. Calcium was titrated with EDTA at 600 mμ in the presence of sodium hydroxide and calcon indicator (C.I. Mordant Black 17) and the total calcium and magnesium with EDTA using eriochrome black T as indicator. Solvent extraction with a continuous extractor was used to separate aluminium, beryllium, bismuth, cadmium, cerium, chromium, cobalt, copper, gallium, indium, iron, lead, mercury, molybdenum, nickel, thallium, thorium, tin, titanium, tungsten, uranium, vanadium, zinc and zirconium, from calcium and magnesium before the titrations. Most of the elements were extracted at about pH 5 as their complexes with 8-hydroxyquinoline using chloroform. Beryllium, cerium and chromium were extracted as acetylacetonates. Manganese which was not removed quantitatively by the solvent extraction process was precipitated as hydrated dioxide by boiling with sodium chlorite. Phosphate, arsenate and selenate were removed by precipitation with excess zirconium nitrate in acid solution. The excess of zirconium was removed as its oxinate during the extraction process.

(c) *Rocks and minerals.* Calcium and magnesium have been determined in agricultural liming materials using an automatic photometric titrator[124]. The calcium was determined by titrating with standard EDTA solution using murexide as indicator. The results for calcium oxide in the range of 30–67% were in good agreement with those obtained by the classical A.O.A.C. method[125]. Magnesium was determined in two ways, namely (a) by subtracting the amount of calcium in the sample from the sum of the calcium and magnesium obtained by photometric titration with EDTA using eriochrome black T as indicator, and (b) by direct titration of magnesium with EDTA after the removal of calcium as oxalate, tungstate or sulphite. The results for magnesium oxide in the range of 2–20% were in good agreement with the classical method[125] using the latter procedure, but by the former procedure the results often differed appreciably from those obtained by the classical method, especially for small amounts of magnesium oxide. Obviously a considerable error is introduced when two relatively large values are subtracted to give a much lower value.

Shapiro and Brannock[57] constructed an automatic photometric titrator for use in the determination of calcium and magnesium in carbonate rocks. The 0·5 g sample was dissolved by the usual treatment with hydrochloric acid, and the solution diluted to a definite volume. A suitable aliquot of the solution was titrated visually with a concentrated EDTA solution in the presence of murexide and sodium hydroxide until just before the end-point. The exact equivalence point was determined by automatic photometric titration with a more dilute solution of EDTA.

Magnesium was determined in another aliquot of the solution after heavy metals in the solution had been removed as hydrated oxides (i.e. removal of R_2O_3) and calcium had been removed as calcium tungstate. The magnesium was titrated in the presence of eriochrome black T as indicator. For further details the original paper should be consulted.

In 0·5 g samples of carbonate rocks, calcium oxide (present as 30–55% of the whole) was determined to within 0·4% of the total contents, and magnesium oxide (present as 0·2–22%) to within 0·04% of the total contents for $<1\%$ and to within 0·2% of the total contents for a magnesium oxide content of 1–22%.

Campen *et al.*[126] have determined water-soluble calcium in gypsum by agitating 1 g of the sample for 2 hr with 1 l. of 1% (w/v) sucrose solution. The calcium in the filtrate was determined by photometric titration with EDTA using murexide as indicator.

Synthetic mixtures of Group II elements and minerals have been analysed for calcium and magnesium by spectrophotometric titration with EDTA after an initial separation using paper chromatography[39]. The calcium and magnesium after removal from the paper were titrated with 0·0025 M EDTA solution at 630 mμ in a solution buffered at pH 10 with ammonia and ammonium chloride in the presence of eriochrome black T as indicator. A measured quantity of standard magnesium chloride solution was added to the calcium solution before the titration in order to obtain a reasonable colour change. Minute traces of iron and other metallic impurities removed from the paper along with the calcium and magnesium were complexed with cyanide.

The method was used to determine calcium oxide in 50 mg samples of dolomite, strontianite and barytocalcite, and magnesium oxide in a 50 mg sample of a dolomite. The authors stated that 1 mg samples of dolomite and 3 mg samples of strontianite or barytocalcite could be analysed if the method was slightly modified. The accuracy was $\pm 1\%$ of the total content for amounts of oxide up to 20%, and $\pm 2\%$ where the amount of oxide exceeded 20%. Strontium or barium, if present in the sample, could be determined by the same procedure.

Calcium and magnesium in slags and limestones have also been determined by photometric titration with EDTA without the removal of those heavy elements which can be masked with triethanolamine[127]. Calcium was titrated in the presence of murexide, and total calcium and magnesium with *o*-cresolphthalein complexan as indicator.

Malmstadt and Hadjiioannou[128] have determined calcium and magnesium in dolomites and limestones using EDTA as a titrant and automatic derivative spectrophotometric end-point termination. The Sargent–Malmstadt spectro-electro titrator (2.6) was used for these titrations. One gram samples of the carbonate minerals were treated with perchloric acid, silica was filtered off and metals which would otherwise interfere in the subsequent titrations were removed as hydrated oxides in the usual manner with ammonium hydroxide. The filtrate was diluted to a definite volume. Calcium was determined in a suitable aliquot of the solution by titrating with EDTA at 650 mμ in the presence of sodium hydroxide and calcon (C.I. Mordant Black 17) as indicator. The total calcium and magnesium in another aliquot was determined by titrating with EDTA, again at 650 mμ, using eriochrome black T as indicator. In both titrations, traces of interfering metal ions were masked with triethanolamine.

The results were excellent. Both calcium and magnesium were determined with an accuracy of $\pm 0{\cdot}1\%$ of the amounts present, provided that the weight ratio of magnesium to calcium did not exceed 1 : 1. When the concentration of magnesium ions in the solution exceeded that of the calcium ions, the calcium results were slightly low, because some calcium hydroxide coprecipitated on the magnesium hydroxide before the calcium titration.

(d) *Water.* A spectrophotometric titration has been applied by

Aconsky and Mori[129] to the determination of calcium in water. The calcium was titrated with standard EDTA solution at 610 mμ using murexide as indicator in a solution of pH about 12·9. 0·1–400 p.p.m. of calcium in water were titrated with reasonable accuracy. Iron (III) and aluminium within 15 p.p.m., copper (II) within 0·3 p.p.m., manganese (II), zinc, magnesium, sulphate and chloride did not affect the results.

Carpenter[130] has determined calcium in sea-water by spectrophotometric EDTA titration at 510 mμ of the calcium in solutions adjusted to pH 11·8 with piperidine; murexide was used as indicator. The calcium had been previously separated from magnesium and strontium, which would otherwise interfere in the method. The Group II elements were separated on a column of Dowex 50 (100–200 mesh, 8 % cross linkage) in the ammonium form by elution with ammonium acetylacetonate solution. The results for the determination of calcium in sea-water by this method were in good agreement (within 0·25 %) with the results obtained by the classical triple oxalate procedure, after making a correction for the strontium content of the oxalate precipitate.

Calcium and magnesium in water have also been determined by Malmstadt and Hadjiioannou[131] using automatic photometric titration with EDTA. Calcium was determined in the presence of magnesium at pH 13 using calcon (Mordant Black 17) as indicator. The total calcium and magnesium was determined at pH 10 with eriochrome black T as indicator. The results for the analyses of samples with total hardness in the range of 0·5 to 600 p.p.m. were reproducible and accurate.

(e) *Alloys.* Magnesium in aluminium alloys has been determined by spectrophotometric titration with EDTA using chrome azurol S (C.I. Mordant Blue 29) as indicator[132]. 0·5–1·0 g of alloy containing 2–3 mg of magnesium were treated with hydrochloric and nitric acids, the solution evaporated to dryness, the residue taken up in water and the silica removed by filtration. The solution was treated with triethanolamine, to complex the aluminium, and with sodium hydroxide–sodium cyanide solution until definitely alkaline. The magnesium hydroxide was filtered off, washed, and dissolved in a small amount of dilute hydrochloric acid solution. The solution was buffered with ammonia and ammonium chloride, traces of other metals were complexed with sodium cyanide and triethanolamine, and the magnesium was titrated at 570 mμ with 0·01 M EDTA using chrome azurol S as indicator. The optical density of the solution due to the magnesium–chrome azurol S lake fell steadily to the equivalence point.

5.6 Cobalt. West and de Vries[21] titrated spectrophotometrically at 510 mμ cobalt (II) nitrate in aqueous solution and in aqueous–alcohol solutions with potassium thiocyanate to study the species formed between these compounds. Breaks in the plot of optical density against the ratio of the concentrations of thiocyanate ion to cobaltous ion occurred at 1 : 1 and 1 : 6, indicating that the species $Co(CNS)^{+}$ and $Co(CNS)_6^{4-}$ had been formed in solution.

5.7 Copper. Sweetser and Bricker[20] determined copper (II) in the presence of many other elements by spectrophotometric titration with EDTA at 745 mμ. The solution was buffered with acetic acid and sodium acetate and the spectrophotometric end-point was based on the fact that at 745 mμ the copper (II)–EDTA complex absorbs more strongly than copper (II) ions themselves. When 30 mg amounts of copper were titrated, little or no interference was noted in the presence of 20 mg of zinc, 20 mg of cadmium, 14 mg of manganese (II), 20 mg of tin (IV) and 5 mg of aluminium. Interference did, however, occur with lead, bismuth, cobalt, nickel and iron (III), although < 10 mg of iron (III) could be complexed with sodium fluoride. By this method, copper in bell metal and bronze was satisfactorily determined. When tin (IV) was present, tartaric acid was added to keep it in solution.

Procedure. To an aliquot of copper (II) solution, containing about 30 mg of copper, in a suitable titration cell, add 20 ml of acetate buffer solution and water to make the volume about 90 ml. The resulting solution should have a pH of 2·4–2·8. Set the wavelength to 745 mμ, start the stirrer into motion and adjust the optical density reading to zero. Titrate the solution with 0·1 M EDTA solution in the usual manner and locate the end-point from a plot of optical density against volume of titrant added.

Underwood[133] has shown that the method of Sweetser and Bricker[20], just described, for the spectrophotometric titration of copper (II) with EDTA at 745 mμ, may be applied to the determination of mixtures of iron (III) and copper (II). When the pH of the solution is about 2 (chloroacetate buffer) the iron (III) is titrated before the copper (II), because iron (III) forms the more stable complex with EDTA. Iron (III) and the iron (III)–EDTA complex do not absorb appreciably at 745 mμ; so the iron (III) end-point was located, on the plot of optical density against volume of titrant added, at the intersection of the horizontal base line and a sharply rising line caused by the increase in optical density of the solution as the concentration of copper (II)–EDTA complex increased. The copper (II) end-point was located at the intersection of this rising line and the horizontal plateau obtained when all of the copper (II) was complexed with EDTA. The method was used to determine iron and copper in an aluminium alloy.

Suk and Miketukova[97] have determined copper (II) by photometric titration with standard EDTA solution in the presence of pyrocatechol violet as indicator. In the vicinity of the end-point the colour of the solution changes from blue to yellow, or to green with large amounts of copper (II). 1–34 mg of copper were determined with a maximum error of 0·08 mg.

Procedure. Add a suitable aliquot of copper (II) solution containing 1–34 mg of metal to a suitable titration cell and dilute to 70–100 ml with distilled water. Add 3–5 ml of 10% (w/v) ammonium nitrate solution and 4–5 drops of indicator solution (0·1% aq.). Add ammonia solution until the appearance of the blue colour of the copper (II)–indicator complex. Then add 5 ml of 20% (w/v) sodium acetate solution. Select a yellow filter, start the stirrer into motion and adjust the optical density reading to a high value. Titrate with 0·002–0·1 M EDTA solution in the usual way, selecting an EDTA solution of concentration suitable for the approximate amount of copper to be expected. Locate the end-point from a plot of optical density against volume of titrant added.

Brasses and bronzes have been analysed for copper and zinc by automatic derivative spectrophotometric titration using the Sargent–Malmstadt spectro-electro titrator (2.6)[80]. The copper alone in an aliquot of the alloy solution was determined by adding potassium iodide crystals and titrating the iodine thus formed with standard sodium thiosulphate solution. This method has already been discussed (4.7).

The sum of copper and zinc was then determined by titrating a hot aliquot of alloy solution, obtained by appropriate treatment of the brass or bronze (see 4.7), and buffered to pH 4·0 with acetic acid and sodium acetate, with standard EDTA solution in the presence of 1-(2-pyridylazo)-2-naphthol as indicator. A wavelength of 575 mμ was used and the titration was terminated automatically when the colour of the solution changed sharply from red to yellow at the end-point, i.e. after the titration of both the copper and zinc.

Copper (II) has also been determined by photometric titration with triethylenetetramine sulphate in the presence of a large number of other metals[134, 135]. Of the common metals only mercury, nickel, cobalt, aluminium and chromium (III) interfered, but copper was titrated in the presence of the first four of these when suitable auxiliary complexing agents were employed. Interference from chromium (III) was prevented by oxidation to chromium (VI). A photometric titration with this reagent was used for the determination of copper in aluminium alloys.

Procedure. Dissolve 0·1 to 0·2 g of alloy, accurately weighed, in the smallest quantity of hydrochloric acid solution. When the aluminium has dissolved add several drops of nitric acid solution and boil to bring the copper into solution. Filter the solution and to the filtrate add sufficient solid sodium citrate to keep the aluminium in solution when it is subsequently made alkaline. Adjust the pH to 10 with ammonia and titrate photometrically at 565 mμ with 0·1 M trien sulphate. Locate the end-point from the usual plot of optical density against volume of titrant added.

Boyle and Robinson[136] have determined copper (II) as nitrate in organic solvents by spectrophotometric titration with a solution of 8-hydroxyquinoline. Titrations were performed in the following media, namely, (a) dimethylformamide-n-butylamine (7 : 1 v/v), and (b) dioxane-n-propyl alcohol-triethylamine-15 N ammonia (16 : 16 : 2 : 1 by volume). Solvent (a) must be anhydrous, but solvent (b) may contain a small proportion of water. The method is based on the fact that the copper (II)–oxine complex has a peak absorption at 400 mμ while oxine itself, in these solvents, absorbs very little at this or higher wavelengths. For solvent (a), the titrant was oxine in dimethylformamide, for solvent (b), oxine in dioxane-n-propyl alcohol (1 : 1 v/v). About 2·5 mg amounts of copper were determined in both solvents to within $\pm$ 0·2%.

5.8 Iron. Iron (III) has been determined by spectrophotometric titration at 525 mμ with EDTA in the presence of an excess of salicylic acid over the iron[20]. The iron (III)–salicylic acid complex absorbs strongly at 525 mμ, but is broken down on the addition of EDTA with the formation of the more stable iron (III)–EDTA complex. When 28 mg of iron were titrated, little or no interference resulted from the presence of 30 mg of zinc, 30 mg of chromium (III), 40 mg of aluminium and 5 mg of manganese (II). Interfering ions were lead, bismuth, cobalt, nickel and copper (II). The method was used to analyse a steel.

Procedure. To an aliquot of iron (III) solution, containing about 30 mg of iron, in a suitable cell, add 20 ml of a suitable buffer solution, so that, when the solution is diluted to about 90 ml with water, its pH will be in the range 1·7–2·3. Set the stirrer in motion and the wavelength to 525 mμ. Adjust the optical density reading to approximately 0·2. Add to the cell 1 ml of salicylic acid solution (6% w/v in acetone). Titrate the solution with 0·1 M EDTA in the usual way and locate the end-point from the plot of optical density against volume of titrant added.

Underwood[133] has reported that the method of Sweetser and Bricker[20] for the spectrophotometric titration of copper (II) with EDTA at 745 mμ (5.7) may be applied to the determination of mixtures of iron (III) and copper (II). This method has already been discussed in connection with copper (II) (see section 5.7 for more details).

Iron (III) in quantities less than 50 mg has been determined by spectrophotometric titration at 610 mμ with EDTA using ferron (7-iodo-8-hydroxyquinoline-5-sulphonic acid) as indicator[137].

Iron (III) and nickel in the same sample of solution have been titrated quantitatively with photometric end-point detection using EDTA[138]. The iron was masked with pyrophosphate and the nickel was titrated directly with EDTA using murexide as indicator. An excess of EDTA was then added to destroy the pyrophosphate complex and the excess was back-titrated with standard nickel nitrate solution.

Underwood[139] has determined 0·2–1·0 mg of iron (III) in 100 ml of solution buffered to pH 3·5 (chloroacetate) by spectrophotometric titration at 470 mμ with 0·01 M ethylenediamine-N,N′-di-(α-*o*-hydroxyphenyl acetate). 470 mμ is the absorption maximum for the red iron (III) chelate. The end-point was located from a plot of optical density against volume of titrant added. The maximum error was 2·6%. In titrations of 0·5 mg of iron, no interference was noted with 50 mg quantities of the following ions, namely, magnesium, calcium, chromium (III), manganese (II), cobalt (II), zinc, cadmium, mercury (II) and lead. Elements which caused some interference were thorium, silver, aluminium, nickel and copper.

5.9 Lead. 0·2–2 mg of lead in 100 ml of solution of pH 2·0 have been determined by spectrophotometric titration at 240 mμ, with 0·001 or 0·01 M EDTA solutions[95]. The maximum error was 1·5%. Such a titration is possible because the lead–EDTA complex has an absorption peak at 240 mμ while free EDTA scarcely absorbs at that wavelength. Mixtures of bismuth and lead were also analysed by this procedure, a wavelength of 240 mμ being chosen. All of the bismuth is titrated before the lead, because the bismuth–EDTA complex is more stable than the lead–EDTA complex. At 240 mμ, bismuth ions absorb slightly, the bismuth–EDTA complex more so, and the lead–EDTA complex the most of these three. Lead ions and free EDTA do not absorb at this wavelength. A plot of optical density against volume of titrant added therefore consisted of three sections, a slight rise as the bismuth was titrated, a much steeper rise as the lead was titrated and a horizontal plateau when all of the lead was complexed. The end-points were located at the intersections of these lines.

5.10 Lithium. Specker *et al.*[140] have shown that lithium chloride in ketone solution may be titrated photometrically with an acetone solution of copper (II) perchlorate. The method is based on the fact that lithium chloride and copper (II) perchlorate form in ketone solution a deep red–orange complex of formula $Li(CuCl_3).xR_2CO$ i.e.

$$3LiCl + Cu(ClO_4)_2 + xR_2CO \rightarrow Li(CuCl_3).xR_2CO + 2LiClO_4$$

The method may be employed for the determination of lithium chloride in mixtures of alkali metal chlorides. The accuracy of the method is good.

Procedure. Shake a finely powdered sample of alkali metal chloride, dried at 120–130°C, for 1 hr with 50 ml of acetone or cyclohexanone. Filter the contents of the flask through a dry filter, wash the residue several times with acetone and make the combined filtrates up to 100 ml in a graduated flask. Pipette into the titration cell of a suitable photometer a suitable aliquot of the lithium chloride solution and make the volume of the solution 25 ml with acetone. (The quantity of lithium in the solution should be such that 2–6 ml of titrant will be required in the titration.) Titrate the solution at 366 mμ with 0·01 or 0·001 M copper (II) perchlorate in acetone and determine the end-point from a plot of optical density against volume of titrant added.

Magnesium. See calcium and magnesium.

5.11 Molybdenum. Headridge[141] has employed a photometric titration for the determination of molybdenum (V). 1–11 mg of molybdenum (V), formed by the reduction of molybdate in hydrochloric acid solution with hydrazine sulphate, were treated with a measured excess of EDTA solution. The excess of EDTA in 30 ml of solution buffered at pH 4·2 was titrated with 0·01 M zinc sulphate solution in a filter photometer at 520 mμ using alizarin complexan (1:2-dihydroxyanthraquinon-3-yl-methylamine-N,N-diacetic acid) as indicator. The molybdenum was determined with an accuracy of ± 0·05 mg.

5.12 Nickel. Boyer[142] constructed a photometric titrator for the determination of excess of cyanide over nickel with silver nitrate solution, using sodium iodide as indicator. The end-point was indicated by a precipitate of silver iodide which was formed when all of the excess cyanide had been complexed by the silver ions. The photometric titration was greatly superior to a visual titration, particularly in the analysis of high-chromium alloys. The accuracy was in the order of 0·1 % for nickel in alloys.

Nickel has been determined by spectrophotometric titration with 0·1 M EDTA at 1000 mμ[20]. The solution was buffered to pH 4·0 with acetic acid and sodium acetate. At 1000 mμ, the nickel–EDTA complex absorbs much more strongly than hydrated nickel ions. About 30 mg quantities of nickel in 90 ml of solution were determined with a maximum error of 0·35 %.

Brake and co-workers[143] determined nickel in the presence of cobalt by a modification of the above method of Sweetser and Bricker[20] where the nickel is titrated spectrophotometrically at 1000 mμ with EDTA solution. Interference from cobalt was prevented by complexing the cobalt with nitroso R salt. No interference resulted from the red cobalt complex because it does not absorb at 1000 mμ. 6–25 mg of nickel were determined in the presence of up to 7 mg of cobalt with 0·1 M EDTA with an error not exceeding 1 %. The determination of 2·5–9·0 mg of nickel in the presence of up to 8 mg of cobalt with 0·03 M EDTA resulted in an error not greater than 1·5 %. Up to 4 mg of manganese (II) and tin (IV) did not interfere in the method. However, interference did occur with silver, copper (II), iron (III), vanadium (IV) and (V), chromium (III), zinc and aluminium.

Procedure. To 30 ml of the nickel and cobalt solution in a 150 ml beaker add 10 ml of sodium acetate solution (50 % w/v) and 40 ml of nitroso R salt solution (1 % w/v). Adjust the pH of the solution to 5–7 with sodium hydroxide and allow to stand for 10 min. Heat the solution to boiling and immediately add 10 ml of 8 N nitric acid. Continue heating for exactly 20 sec (to destroy the nickel–nitroso R salt complex and excess of the reagent). Remove and cool rapidly to room temperature in an ice-bath. Adjust the pH to 3·5–4·0 with saturated sodium hydroxide solution. Transfer the solution to a suitable titration cell and dilute to 120 ml. Set the stirrer in motion, adjust the wavelength to 1000 mμ and set the optical density to zero. Titrate in the usual way with standard EDTA solution locating the equivalence point from a plot of optical density against volume of titrant added.

Photometric titration with EDTA has also been used by Dewald[138] for the analysis of solutions containing both nickel and iron (III). For further details consult section 5.8.

5.13 Palladium. Spectrophotometric titration was employed by West and Amis[22] to determine the composition of the compound produced by the reaction of palladium (II) chloride with pararosaniline hydrochloride. A plot of optical density against moles of palladium/moles of pararosaniline hydrochloride had a break at 1·5, showing that the reaction product was $2C_{19}H_{17}N_3HCl.3PdCl_2$.

5.14 Rare Earths. Lane and Fritz[2] have determined 10 μg to 40 mg amounts of rare earths in 100 ml of solution by spectrophotometric titration with EDTA at 570 mμ using arsenazo (2-(1,8-dihydroxy-3,6-disulpho-2-naphthylazo)-benzene arsonic acid) as indicator. The method is based on the fact that at 570 mμ rare earth–arsenazo complexes absorb strongly, while the absorption of free arsenazo at that wavelength is much less. The titrations were carried out in solutions buffered at pH 6 with pyridine. The concentration of the titrant varied from 10^{-5} M to 0·05 M depending on the weight of rare earth being titrated, but a concentration was generally chosen such that about 5 ml of titrant was required at the equivalence point. With amounts of rare earths in excess of 1 mg the equivalence point could have been obtained by a visual titration, but for the titration of microgram quantities, spectrophotometric end-point location was essential. The accuracy was good. For quantities of rare earths less than 30 μg the technique of instrument scale expansion, as described by Reilley and Crawford[144], was applied.

The spectrophotometric titration of rare earths with EDTA can also be carried out in the presence of an equal molar quantity or less of uranyl ion, if enough arsenazo is added to the solution to complex all of the uranium and enough of the rare earths to give a measurable colour change. The uranyl–arsenazo complex is not titrated with EDTA.

Rare earths have been determined by photometric back-titration of an excess of EDTA over the rare earths, with lanthanum nitrate as titrant and sodium alizarin sulphonate as indicator[58]. A simple filter photometer was constructed for this purpose with a device for recording the titration curves. A filter with maximum transmission at 520 mμ was employed. At this wavelength, the lanthanum–indicator complex absorbs strongly. 0·2–10 mg amounts of the oxides of lanthanum, cerium, europium, dysprosium and erbium, and 0·2–170 mg of mixed oxides from the cerium group, were satisfactorily determined.

Procedure. Take a sample containing not more than about 200 mg of rare earth oxides (as perchlorate, chloride or nitrate) in about 200 ml of solution in a suitable titration cell. Add 1 ml of hydroxylamine hydrochloride solution (2% w/v) (to prevent oxidation of cerium (III)), 0·5 ml of indicator solution (0·05% w/v) and 1 ml of buffer solution (1 M in both acetic acid and sodium acetate). Adjust the pH of the solution to 4·6. Heat to 85°C and maintain this temperature during the titration. Start the stirrer and add either 0·025 M or 0·0025 M EDTA solution until the end-point is passed. Again adjust the pH of the solution to 4·6. Set the optical density reading to zero and back-titrate with 0·0025 M lanthanum nitrate solution. Locate the end-point in the usual way.

Photometric titration with EDTA using sodium alizarin sulphonate may also be employed to determine mixtures of rare earths and thorium. The procedure is discussed under thorium (5.18).

10 μg quantities of rare earths have been titrated quantitatively with EDTA with photometric end-point detection at 580 mμ, using xylenol orange as indicator[145]. The method was an adaptation of the procedure already described by Körbl and Pribil[146] for milligram quantities. The titrations were performed in cells of 0·5 ml capacity, containing just over 0·4 ml of solution buffered to pH 5·8 with sodium acetate and acetic acid. (For the titration of lanthanum the pH of the solution should be 5·2.) Before the addition of 10 μl. of solution containing the rare earths, a blank titration was made in the buffered solution to titrate minute traces of impurities. The results for the titration of 10 μg amounts of lanthanum, cerium, praseodymium, neodymium, samarium and gadolinium were in good agreement with those obtained for the titration of much larger volumes of the same solutions by the macro-method of Körbl and Pribil.

5.15 Scandium. Fritz and Pietrzyk[147] have determined scandium by spectrophotometric titration with EDTA at 745 mμ in the presence of copper (II) as indicator. The scandium–EDTA complex is more stable than the copper (II)–EDTA complex; hence the scandium is titrated before the copper (II). After the end-point the optical density of the solution increases, because the copper (II)–EDTA complex absorbs strongly at 745 mμ. The method was used to determine scandium in the presence of rare earths, which form EDTA complexes considerably less stable than the scandium–EDTA complex. Large amounts of aluminium, calcium, magnesium, uranium (VI), nitrate, chloride and perchlorate did not interfere in the method. Interference occurred with bismuth, thorium, hafnium, zirconium, sulphate and fluoride. Interference from small amounts of iron (III) is prevented by reducing the iron to the ferrous state. The average error is $\pm$ 0·5%.

Procedure. To a suitable titration cell add an aliquot of acid solution containing 4–11 mg of scandium. Add 4 ml of 0·05 M copper (II) nitrate solution, adjust the pH to 3·0 with sodium hydroxide solution, and dilute to 75 ml. Place the cell in a spectrophotometer, set the stirrer in motion and adjust the wavelength to 745 mμ and the optical density reading to zero. Titrate the solution in the usual way with 0·03 M EDTA solution and determine the end-point graphically.

5.16 Silver. An indirect photometric titration has been used for the determination of silver[148]. In ammoniacal solution, silver reacts with excess of potassium tetracyanonickelate (II) to produce an equivalent amount of nickel, which may be titrated photometrically with EDTA using murexide as indicator. Most metal ions except those of sodium and potassium interfere in the method. 0·1–10 mg of silver were determined with an error not exceeding 0·03 mg.

Procedure. Dissolve approximately 25 mg of potassium tetracyanonickelate (II) in a little water in a suitable titration cell. Add about 5 ml of concentrated ammonium hydroxide solution and 1 murexide tablet (murexide–potassium chloride). Crush the tablet and stir to get the solid into solution. Dilute the solution to 70 ml. Select a wavelength of about 435 mμ and set the optical density reading to zero. Add 0·1–10 mg of silver in approximately 15 ml of solution. (The pH of the silver solution should be such that the quantity of ammonium hydroxide in the solution in the cell during the titration should correspond to 3–10 ml of concentrated reagent.) The optical density of the solution at once increases. Titrate the solution with 0·005 M EDTA for $>$ 1 mg of silver and with 0·0006 M EDTA if $\leqslant$ 1 mg of silver is present. Record the optical density readings after suitable additions of titrant, and obtain the end-point from a plot of optical density against volume of titrant added. The end-point is located where the line of decreasing optical density intersects the zero optical density line. No error is introduced from dilution of the solution during the titration.

5.17 Strontium. Headridge and Magee[39] have used a spectrophotometric titration for the determination of strontium after its separation from other Group II elements by paper chromatography. The strontium after removal from the chromatographic paper was titrated with EDTA at 630 mμ, using eriochrome black T as indicator in a solution buffered at pH 10 with ammonia and ammonium chloride. Since strontium does not form a stable complex with eriochrome black T, a known amount of magnesium was added to the solution in order to obtain a satisfactory change in optical density during the titration. Minute traces of iron and certain other metallic impurities removed from the paper along with the strontium were complexed with cyanide.

The method was used to determine strontium oxide in a 50 mg sample of strontianite, and the authors stated that a 3 mg sample could be analysed if a slight modification in the method was employed. Magnesium, calcium and barium, if present in the sample, may be determined by the same procedure.

5.18 Thorium. Malmstadt and Gohrbrandt[46] have determined thorium by automatic spectrophotometric titration, at 320 mμ, of an excess of EDTA over thorium with standard copper (II) nitrate solution. The titration was made in a solution buffered to pH about 4·6 with sodium acetate and acetic acid. The method depends on the facts that, at 320 mμ, free EDTA, the thorium–EDTA complex, and the copper (II)–acetate complex do not absorb appreciably while the copper (II)–EDTA complex absorbs strongly. The maximum error was 0·15%. The instructions in the following method apply to a manual titration. For details of the automatic titration the original paper should be consulted.

Procedure. Pipette a suitable aliquot of thorium solution containing 1–50 mg of the metal into a suitable titration cell and add a known volume of standard 0·01 M EDTA solution such that a slight excess is present. Add 1 ml of sodium acetate–acetic acid buffer (0·2 M with respect to each compound) and dilute the solution to 100–150 ml. Set the stirrer in motion, and adjust the wavelength to 320 mμ and the optical density to zero. Titrate the excess of EDTA with standard 0·01 M copper (II) nitrate solution recording the optical density readings after suitable additions of titrant. Obtain the equivalence point from the plot of optical density against volume of titrant added.

Thorium–cerium binary alloys have been analysed for thorium by photometric titration of an excess of EDTA over the thorium, in a solution of the alloy, with standard thorium perchlorate solution using eriochrome cyanine (C.I. Mordant Blue 3) as indicator[149]. At pH 2·2 there was no interference from cerium.

Procedure. Obtain the thorium and cerium from the alloy as perchlorates in aqueous solution, the cerium being in the cerous state. Dilute a suitable aliquot of the solution containing 10–150 mg of thorium to 400 ml in a suitable titration cell and add 2 ml of 0·1% (w/v) eriochrome cyanine indicator solution. Add 0·02 M EDTA solution from a burette until the end-point, denoted by a gradual change in colour from purple to orange, is exceeded by 1–2 ml. Then adjust the pH of the solution to 2·2 using ammonia or perchloric acid solutions. Set the stirrer in motion and the wavelength to 546 mμ. Adjust the optical density reading to 1·0 and titrate with 0·02 M thorium perchlorate solution, recording the optical density readings after suitable additions of titrant. Obtain the end-point from a plot of optical density against volume of titrant added.

Thorium has also been determined in perchloric acid solutions of thorium and tungsten, by photometric titration at 550 mμ of an excess of EDTA over the thorium, with thorium nitrate solution using sodium alizarin sulphonate as indicator[150]. The tungsten was kept in solution at pH 2·8 as the soluble tungsten (VI)–hydrogen peroxide complex.

Bril and co-workers[58] have also used sodium alizarin sulphonate as an indicator for the determination of thorium by photometric titration, at 520 mμ, with EDTA solution. A device for recording titration curves was incorporated in their photometer. 0·1–150 mg of thorium oxide were determined with a maximum error of ± 0·1 mg for amounts in excess of 10 mg and of ± 0·01 mg for quantities in the range 0·1–10 mg. Lead, uranium (VI) and sulphate ions did not interfere in the method.

Procedure. To not more than 200 mg of thorium oxide (as perchlorate, chloride or nitrate) in about 200 ml of solution in a suitable titration cell, add a known amount of EDTA calculated on the basis of a rough visual titration, so that no more than 5 ml of 0·0025 M EDTA solution will be consumed before the end-point is reached in the accurate photometric titration. Add 0·5 ml of sodium alizarin sulphonate solution (0·05% w/v), set the stirrer in motion and adjust the pH to 2·8. Set the wavelength to 520 mμ and the optical density reading to 1·0. Titrate the solution with 0·0025 M EDTA solution and locate the end-point graphically in the usual way.

Note. These workers also determined thorium by adding an excess of EDTA and back-titrating with standard thorium nitrate solution. They also determined thorium in the presence of cerium group rare earths (up to europium) by methods similar to those just described. At pH 2·8, these rare earths were not titrated with EDTA. The solution was then analysed for rare earths by the method already described in section 5.14 (Bril *et al.*) after adjusting the pH to 3·7.

Thorium has also been determined by a procedure based on an initial spectrophotometric titration of a standard EDTA solution with standard thorium nitrate solution, in the presence of chrome azurol S (C.I. Mordant Blue 29) as indicator, for the construction of a calibration curve of optical density against volume of thorium nitrate solution added[151]. A solution containing an unknown quantity of thorium is added to the same amount of EDTA and indicator as are used for the calibration curve, and the solution is titrated with the standard thorium nitrate solution until the end-point has been passed. The optical density of the solution is then measured, and from the calibration curve the total quantity of thorium, initially added, is obtained by subtraction. By this method, 50–150 mg of thorium were determined with an error not exceeding 0·3 mg.

Menis *et al.*[48] have applied automatic spectrophotometric end-point detection to the titration of 2–33 μg of thorium with EDTA using quercetin as indicator. A coefficient of variation of about 1% was obtained. No interference occurred with less than 100 μg amounts of aluminium, calcium, cobalt, chromium (III) and (VI), mercury (II), uranium (VI) and zinc. Interference was caused by the presence of 100 μg amounts of iron (II) and (III), manganese (II), molybdenum (VI), nickel and titanium (IV), although no interference resulted from the presence of certain of these elements in lower concentration. Chlorides, perchlorates and nitrates do not affect the titration but fluoride, phosphate, acetate and sulphate must be absent. These workers employed a double beam instrument with a comparison solution in order to operate the instrument at maximum sensitivity. The method given below applies to a manual titration with a single beam spectrophotometer.

Procedure. To an aliquot of solution containing 2–33 μg of thorium, in a suitable titration cell, add 1 ml of quercetin solution (0·1% in absolute alcohol) and 10 ml of ethyl alcohol. Dilute the solution to about 35 ml with water and adjust the pH to 3·0 with perchloric acid or sodium carbonate solution. Allow the colour to develop for 10 min. Set the wavelength to 422 mμ and the optical density reading to a high value. Start the stirrer and titrate the solution with 0·001 M EDTA solution, recording the optical density readings after suitable additions of titrant. Locate the end-point from a plot of optical density against volume of titrant added.

5.19 Titanium. 0·3–3 mg of titanium (IV) have been titrated photometrically at 450 mμ with 0·05 M EDTA in 0·05 N sulphuric acid solution in the presence of a few drops of hydrogen peroxide (30% w/v)[152]. A stable titanium (IV)–hydrogen peroxide–EDTA complex was formed. However, Sweetser and Bricker[98] had previously reported that such a titration has few advantages over other existing volumetric and photometric procedures for titanium.

5.20 Vanadium. Hartkamp[153] has determined vanadium (V) by photometric titration at 432 mμ, with pyridine-2:6-dicarboxylic acid in the presence of hydrogen peroxide. In dilute mineral acid solution a 1 : 1 : 1 vanadium (V)–hydrogen peroxide–titrant complex was produced. For 0·1–2 mg of vanadium the error was 2%. All but traces of titanium interfere as do four-fold excesses of niobium, tantalum, thorium, tin, zirconium, antimony and copper. The titration has been applied to the determination of vanadium in steel.

Procedure. Dissolve a sample of steel containing 0·3–2 mg of vanadium in 15 ml of aqua regia, dilute to 40 ml, filter if necessary and wash the residue several times with water. Transfer the solution (70–80 ml) to a suitable titration cell and add 0·5–2 ml of hydrogen peroxide solution (30% w/v) and several ml of phosphoric acid solution. Set the stirrer in motion, the wavelength to 432 mμ and the optical density reading to zero. Titrate in the usual way with 0·02 M pyridine-2:6-dicarboxylic acid solution and locate the end-point from the plot of optical density against volume of titrant added.

5.21 Zinc. Sweetser and Bricker[98] have titrated zinc spectrophotometrically at 222 or 228 mμ with EDTA solution. No indicator was required because, in a solution buffered to pH 10, the uncomplexed EDTA absorbs more strongly than the zinc–EDTA complex, and the optical density of the solution increases much more rapidly after the end-point. 0·6–6 mg amounts of zinc were determined with a maximum error of 0·35%.

Procedure. Add an aliquot of solution containing 0·6–6 mg of zinc to a suitable titration cell and add 2 ml of ammonia–ammonium chloride solution. Dilute the solution to 90–100 ml when the pH should be 10. Set the wavelength to 222 or 228 mμ (for 0·001 or 0·01 M EDTA solutions respectively) and start the stirrer into motion. Set the optical density reading to zero, and titrate the solution with standard EDTA solution in the usual way, using 0·001 M EDTA for small quantities of zinc and 0·01 M EDTA for larger amounts. Locate the end-point from a plot of optical density against volume of titrant added. Carry out a blank titration without the added zinc, and subtract the small blank titre from the titre of the previous titration, to obtain the volume of standard EDTA solution equivalent to the zinc in the added aliquot of solution.

Hunter and Miller[19] have also determined zinc by spectrophotometric titration with EDTA, but they employed eriochrome black T as indicator. 0·1–10 mg amounts of zinc were satisfactorily titrated. These workers used the method primarily to determine zinc in aluminium alloys, bronzes, white metal and glass, after the separation of zinc from many of the other elements by anion exchange chromatography and solvent extraction. Excellent results were obtained in these determinations, but the original paper should be consulted for more details. The method now given applies to a spectrophotometric titration of zinc in simple solutions.

Procedure. Add an aliquot of solution containing 0·1–1 mg of zinc to a suitable titration cell. Raise the hydrochloric acid content to 5 ml of 2 N, add ammonia to increase the pH to between 9 and 10, dilute with water to 100 ml and add 0·1 ml of eriochrome black T solution (0·1% w/v in pyridine). Place the cell in the compartment of a spectrophotometer and set the wavelength to 665 mμ. Start the stirrer and adjust the optical density reading to zero. Add small increments of titrant to the solution and record the optical density readings after each addition. Locate the end-point graphically in the usual manner. Carry out a blank titration to determine the small amount of titratable impurities in the reagents.

Boyle and Robinson[136] have titrated spectrophotometrically zinc as nitrate in certain organic solvents with a solution of 8-hydroxyquinoline. The solvents and conditions were almost identical to those already described for the titration of copper (II) with 8-hydroxyquinoline (5.7—Boyle *et al.*). About 25 mg of zinc were determined to within ± 0·2%.

Lubricating oils have been analysed for zinc by spectrophotometric titration with dithizone solution[154]. Suitable aliquots of diluted oil solution containing 30–50 μg of zinc were employed in the titrations. Alkaline earths and alkali metals do not interfere in the method. The results were in good agreement with those obtained by a polarographic procedure.

Procedure. Dilute about 0·1 g of oil to 25 ml with benzene containing 8% of methanol. Add an aliquot of this solution containing 30–50 μg of zinc to a suitable titration cell containing 50 ml of benzene saturated with ammonium acetate and 2 ml of methanol. Set the wavelength to 640 mμ, start the stirrer and adjust the optical density reading to zero. Titrate the solution with dithizone solution (0·05% w/v in benzene) which has been standardized against a standard solution of zinc acetate in methanol. Add 0·1 ml increments and record the optical density of the solution after each addition of titrant. Locate the end-point graphically in the usual way.

5.22 Zirconium. Sweetser and Bricker[98] have determined zirconium by adding an excess of EDTA solution and determining the uncomplexed EDTA by a spectrophotometric back-titration with ferric ammonium sulphate solution in the presence of salicylic acid as indicator. About 5 mg amounts of zirconium were determined with an error not exceeding 0·7%.

Procedure. To a suitable titration cell, add 10 ml of standard EDTA solution (about 0·01 M) and 15 ml of sodium acetate solution (5% w/v). Add an aliquot of zirconium solution containing not more than 8 mg of the metal and 1 ml of salicylic acid solution (6% w/v in acetone) followed by enough water to make the total volume 85–90 ml. Add 3 N ammonium hydroxide slowly to the solution with stirring until the pH is 4·0. Set the wavelength to 520 to 525 mμ, start the stirrer and adjust the optical density reading to zero. Titrate the excess of EDTA with 0·01 M iron (III) solution in the usual manner. Locate the end-point from the plot of optical density against volume of titrant added.

Milner and Edwards[45] have also determined an excess of EDTA over zirconium, by a photometric back-titration with iron (III) solution using salicylic acid (added as sodium salicylate) as indicator. They report that sodium salicylate may be used in solutions of pH 3–7, with an optimum pH of 4. At pH 4, 9 mg amounts and 22 mg amounts of zirconium were each determined five times with a standard deviation of the mean of 0·04 mg. However, at pH 4, more elements interfere in the method than at a lower pH and these workers found that it was more useful to determine zirconium by photometric titration of an excess of EDTA over the zirconium with iron (III) solution. Potassium benzohydroxamate, which may be employed in solutions of pH 1·8–3·3 with pH 2·3 as the optimum pH for photometric titration, was used as indicator. In the titration of 10 mg amounts of zirconium, interference occurred with similar weights of aluminium, bismuth, thorium, tin (II) and (IV), titanium (IV) and cerium (IV), but no interference resulted from the presence of 10 mg of molybdenum (VI) or 500 mg amounts of cerium (III) or uranium (VI). 10–100 mg of zirconium were determined with an accuracy of $\pm$ 0·6% or better. Since uranyl ions did not interfere in the titration, the procedure was applied to the direct determination of zirconium in zirconium–uranium alloys. Results in good agreement with a gravimetric method were obtained.

Procedure. To an aliquot of zirconium solution containing 10–100 mg of the metal, add a few millilitres of concentrated sulphuric acid and evaporate to fumes of sulphuric acid. Cool the solution, dilute with distilled water, transfer to a suitable titration cell and immediately add a measured excess of 0·02 M EDTA solution. Dilute the solution to about 300 ml and adjust the pH to 2·3 by the addition of dilute ammonia solution. Add 1 ml of potassium benzohydroxamate solution (2·5% w/v). Start the stirrer, select a wavelength of 520 mμ and adjust the optical density reading to zero. Titrate the solution with 0·02 M iron (III) solution in the usual way and locate the end-point graphically.

Milner and Sneddon[155] have also applied this back-titration method for the determination of zirconium in zirconium–cerium alloys. At pH 2·2 and using potassium benzohydroxamate as indicator, there is no interference from cerium.

The same back-titration has also been employed by Milner and Barnett[156] for the determination of zirconium in uranium–molybdenum–zirconium, uranium–titanium–zirconium, and uranium–niobium–zirconium alloys. Before the titration procedure was applied, it was found necessary to separate the zirconium from the other constituents in the alloys. This was achieved by a double precipitation of the zirconium as barium fluozirconate from nitric–hydrofluoric acid solutions of the alloys. The zirconium was recovered in a suitable solution for the subsequent titration, by dissolving the barium fluozirconate in nitric–boric acid solution, precipitating the zirconium as hydroxide, dissolving the precipitate in hydrochloric acid solution, fuming the solution with perchloric acid to ensure complete removal of fluoride ions, and diluting to 25–50 ml with water. The zirconium was determined by adding an excess of EDTA solution and back-titrating the excess with standard iron (III) solution, using sodium benzohydroxamate as indicator. The method was also suitable for determining zirconium in the presence of tantalum, tungsten, lead, iron, copper and tin.

Zirconium has been determined by adding a measured excess of EDTA to a suitable aliquot of solution at pH 1–2 and back-titrating at 450 mμ with bismuth nitrate solution employing potassium iodide as indicator[96]. After the end-point the bismuth in excess combined with iodide to form the yellow bismuth–iodide complex, which absorbs appreciably at 450 mμ. (For the photometric titration of bismuth with EDTA using iodide as indicator see section 5.3—Milner and Bacon.) Zirconium in a fluoride-containing solution was also determined by adding an excess of EDTA solution, followed by beryllium sulphate solution, and then back-titrating the solution whose pH had been adjusted to 3·0, with standard bismuth nitrate solution. The end-point was determined photometrically. The beryllium ions complexed preferentially with fluoride ions which, in the absence of beryllium, interfere completely with the determination.

Finally two anions have been determined by photometric titration.

5.23 Cyanide. Brandstetr and Kotrly[157] have determined cyanide photometrically with silver nitrate solution using potassium iodide as indicator. 0·7–80 mg were determined in 90 ml of solution using a photometer with a blue filter. The average error was $\pm$ 0·2%. Chloride and phosphate did not interfere.

5.24 Nitrilotriacetate. Small amounts of nitrilotriacetate were determined by a photometric titration with copper (II) sulphate solution, using catechol violet or murexide as indicator[158].

CHAPTER 6

PRECIPITATION REACTIONS

6.1 Photometric titrations involving precipitation of the titrant can be divided into two types, namely, (A) titrations to maximum turbidity where the controls of the instrument are set to measure changes in the optical density of the solution caused by the formation of precipitate, and (B) titrations involving a colour change in an indicator after the equivalence point, i.e. when all of the ion originally in solution has been precipitated by the titrant. In this second type of titration, a further and more rapid increase in the optical density of the solution occurs as excess of titrant forms a coloured complex or lake with the indicator. Here, the controls of the photometer are set primarily to detect the increase in optical density owing to the formation of coloured complex or lake.

The titration of sulphate with barium ions according to the method of Wickbold[159] is an example of a type A titration (Fig. 20). Titration of fluoride with thorium ions using sodium 2-(*p*-sulphophenylazo)-1:8-dihydroxynaphthalene-3:6-disulphonate as indicator serves to illustrate the type B titration (Fig. 21)[160].

Almost all titrations of type B have been performed in the last decade, and spectrophotometers have often been employed to measure the changes in optical density of the solution caused by the formation of the indicator–titrant complex or lake. In many respects, these titrations are similar to complexometric titrations, and the most satisfactory results are obtained when spectrophotometers are employed for end-point location. Type B titrations are carried out for the quantitative determination of a substance.

With type A titrations, the insoluble precipitate produced is often white and the titrant colourless, making the use of monochromatic or filtered light unnecessary. If the precipitate or titrant is coloured, more satisfactory plots of optical density against volume of titrant added often result if a filter photometer is employed. Spectrophotometers are seldom used for type A titrations.

Type A titrations are employed for two purposes. Firstly, they may be used to study the composition and solubility of precipitates. These turbidimetric titrations are particularly useful for obtaining such information and Bobtelsky[10] has done a great deal of work in this field. He, however, prefers to classify his type of work as heterometry, the titrations being heterometric titrations. These titrations are very similar to turbidimetric titrations performed by other workers.

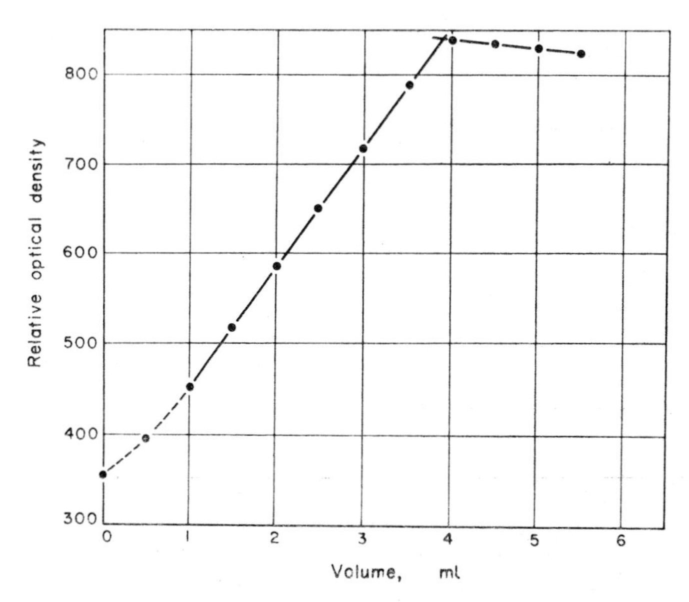

FIG. 20. Titration of about 195 μg of sulphur (as sulphate) with approx. 0·0016 M barium chloride solution

Secondly, type A titrations may be carried out for the quantitative determination of a substance. Most turbidimetric titrations made before 1950 were for this purpose, but the majority of these were performed with pure solutions and often at only one concentration. For such systems results of reasonable accuracy and precision were obtained. However, if turbidimetric titration (type A) is to be widely accepted as a useful analytical technique, it is essential that good results should be obtained when the technique is applied to the quantitative determination of a particular element in a fairly complex solution from, say, an ore. Bobtelsky[10] has reported that a fixed amount of many ions can be quantitatively determined with reasonable accuracy by turbidimetric titration in the presence of large amounts of other ions, but, as yet, the method has hardly been used for the analysis of minerals, alloys, etc. It would be interesting to have information about the accuracy and precision of the method when applied to the analysis of such materials.

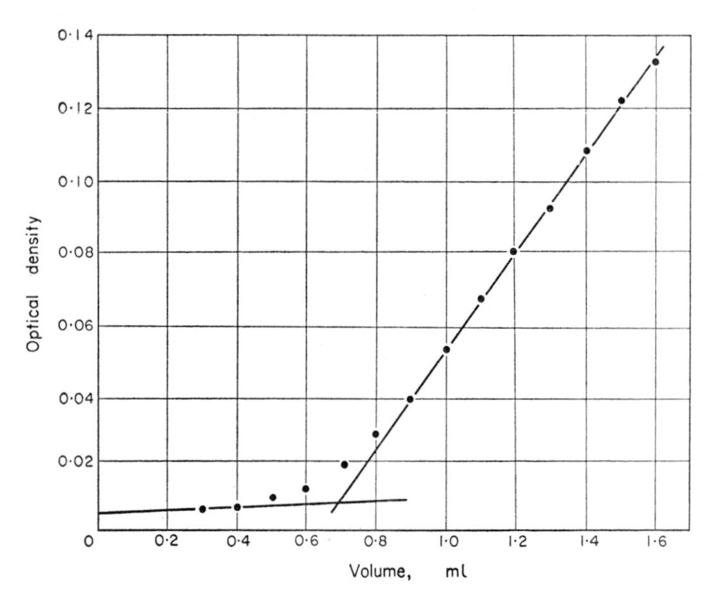

FIG. 21. Titration of about 33 μg of fluoride with 0·001 M thorium nitrate solution at 580 mμ (indicator: SPADNS). (By courtesy of *Analytical Chemistry*)

At the present time it would therefore appear that analytical methods involving type A titrations are not generally suitable, if results of very good accuracy are desired. This applies particularly to systems containing foreign ions for these ions often interfere markedly in the turbidimetric titrations. However, as a quick method for the quantitative determination of ions where a high degree of accuracy is not required, the technique may have its uses. Certainly only a few minutes are required for a titration.

In much of the early work, plots of optical density against volume of titrant added were not used, the authors taking the end-point at maximum turbidity as shown by a galvanometer reading.

A true picture of the conditions prevalent during a titration can, however, only be obtained from a plot of optical density against volume of titrant added. From such a plot the equivalence point can be determined with much greater accuracy. Much of the work on photometric titrations involving precipitation reactions, reported before 1950, is now no longer of interest with the advent of superior methods, and papers published before that time will not be mentioned unless they contain information of potential value.

The processes of nucleation and crystal growth during a turbidimetric titration are not sufficiently understood for the shapes of titration curves to be calculated for a particular system with any degree of exactness. However, Fischer *et al.*[161] have applied a logical argument to type A titrations, in order to predict the shapes of the curves of optical density against volume of titrant added, for various conditions of nucleation and crystal growth. They predicted that any factor which enhanced nucleation at the expense of crystal growth would produce a more satisfactory curve for end-point location. One such factor was the presence of a detergent, e.g. Tergitol or Triton, which was apparently absorbed on the crystal surfaces, thereby minimising further crystal growth. The prediction was verified with some precipitation reactions, but the authors stated that many systems were not affected by a detergent. Protective colloids such as gelatine presumably minimise further crystal growth in a similar way.

It will be noted from the later material in this chapter that some workers have, in fact, employed protective colloids in their systems in order to improve the shape of the titration curves. While protective colloids are useful in certain cases where turbidimetric titrations are being employed for the quantitative determination of a substance such agents should not be employed if the technique is used to study the composition and solubility of precipitates. Bobtelsky has stressed this in his book[162].

Type A titrations

6.2 Bobtelsky and co-workers have dominated this field. The results of their investigations have been fully dealt with in his book on heterometry[10] and that material will not be duplicated here. However, for completeness, a list of the systems which have been investigated by Bobtelsky is given in Table 2. Turbidimetric titrations, carried out by other workers, are also discussed in this section.

TABLE 2

Titrand	Titrant	Titrand	Titrant
Aluminium	citrate[163], phthalate[164, 165], ammonium aurintricarboxylate[166]	Magnesium	8-hydroxyquinoline[196]
Bismuth	sodium diethyldithiocarbamate[167], pyramidon[168], thiocarbanilide[169]	Mercury (II)	mercaptobenzthiazole[197, 198, 199], sodium diethyldithiocarbamate[200, 201], *p*-dimethylamino-benzylidene-rhodanine[202]
Cadmium	sodium diethyldithiocarbamate[170]	Molybdic acid	α-benzoin oxime[203]
Calcium	phthalate[171], sulphuric acid[172]	Nickel	dimethylglyoxime[204, 205], malonate[206] succinate[206]
Cerium (III)	citrate[173]	Palladium	α-nitroso-β-naphthol[207], dimethylglyoxime[208], nitron[185, 209], dithio-oxamide[186], sodium diethyldithiocarbamate[187, 188], benzidine[210]
Chromium (III)	phthalate[164, 165], ammonium aurintricarboxylate[166]	Platinum	nitron[185], sodium diethyldithiocarbamate[187, 188]
Cobalt	α-nitroso-β-naphthol[174, 175], malonate[176], succinate[176], phthalate[176]	Silver	*p*-dimethylamino-benzylidene-rhodanine[211]
Copper (II)	8-hydroxyquinoline[177, 178], sodium quinoline-α-carboxylate[179], salicylaldoxime[180, 181], dithio-oxamide[182], sodium diethyldithiocarbamate[183], malonate[184], phthalate[184]	Sulphuric acid	barium nitrate[212]
Gold (III)	nitron[185], dithio-oxamide[186], sodium diethyldithiocarbamate[187, 188], fuchsine[189]	Thorium	oxalate[213, 214, 215], phthalate[216], maleate[216], citrate[217], tartrate[218]
Iron (III)	phthalate[164, 165], ammonium aurintricarboxylate[166], α-nitroso-β-naphthol[190], citrate[163], nitron[191]	Tungstic acid	fuchsine[189]
Lead	tartrate[192], citrate[163, 193, 194], sodium diethyldithiocarbamate[195]	Uranium (VI)	potassium ferrocyanide[219], disodium phosphate[220]
		Vanadic acid	fuchsine[189]
		Zinc	sodium diethyldithiocarbamate[221], sodium quinoline-α-carboxylate[222]
		Zirconium	oxalate[213, 214, 215]

The reactions of many metal ions with pyro- and tri-phosphate were also investigated by Bobtelsky *et al.*[223, 224, 225].

6.3 Barium. Ringbom[226] has shown that about 1·4 mg of barium as chloride in 30–75 ml of aqueous–alcoholic solution containing gum arabic may be determined by turbidimetric titration with 0·01 M sodium sulphate solution with an error not exceeding 0·4%. The effect of certain foreign ions on the recovery was also examined.

6.4 Calcium. Frey[227] determined calcium in the presence of magnesium, when the concentration of magnesium was less than that of calcium, by photometric titration with ammonium oxalate solution. However, the method is not really satisfactory, because the apparent end-point occurs before the equivalence point, and an empirical correction factor must be employed if reasonable results are to be obtained.

6.5. Fluoride. Fluoride has been determined by turbidimetric titration with calcium or thorium ions using a home-made photometer[228]. 0·2 M calcium chloride was preferred as a titrant for fluoride concentrations between 0·01 and 0·09 M. For the range 0·05 to 0·09 M fluoride, the error was $\pm 1\%$ and this increased to $\pm 4\%$ for 0·01 M solutions. For fluoride ions in the range 0·09–1·0 M, thorium nitrate was employed as titrant. With this reagent the error was $\pm 1\%$ for the range 0·09–0·12 M fluoride, increasing to $\pm 4\%$ for 1·0 M fluoride. No interference was observed for 0·1 M solutions of borate, chloride, bromide, acetate, nitrate or zinc ions but interferences resulted when the solution contained 0·1 M sulphate, phosphate, oxalate, tartrate, hydroxide, iron, lead or magnesium ions. The titrations were satisfactory in the pH range 1–7. The time for a single determination was less than 10 min. End-points were obtained from the usual plot of optical density against volume of titrant added.

6.6 Lead. Lur'e and Tal[229] have used a photometer to detect the end-point in the turbidimetric titration of lead with normal ammonium molybdate solution. The equivalence point coincided with the maximum turbidity when 0·8–8 mg of lead were present in a solution containing gelatine. The method was applicable to the analysis of ores.

6.7 Palladium. 0·1–1·0 mg of palladium have been determined in 30 ml of 95% ethyl alcohol by turbidimetric titration with

0·001–0·005 M 5-iminothiazoline-2-thiamide[230]. In the presence of EDTA, large amounts of calcium, barium, zinc, manganese, cobalt, iron (III), chromium, lead, platinum (IV), copper, cerium (III) and cadmium did not interfere with the determination. The error was never more than ± 3·5%.

6.8 Potassium. Karrman and co-workers[13] have determined 4–28 μg of potassium in pure solution and in blood serum by adding an excess of sodium tetraphenylborate to the solution containing potassium, allowing the precipitate of potassium tetraphenylborate to settle, and titrating spectrophotometrically a suitable aliquot of supernatant solution with cetyltrimethylammonium bromide solution. A colloidal precipitate of cetyltrimethylammonium tetraphenylborate was produced. The end-point was obtained from a plot of optical density against volume of titrant added. The plot was not of the usual shape. A gradual rise to a steady optical density was expected, but in the actual titration, the optical density scarcely changed until 90% of the sodium tetraphenylborate was titrated. Then there was a sudden and sharp rise in optical density to the true equivalence point, after which the optical density readings were steady. Karrman *et al.*, however, preferred to take the end-point to a position half-way up the rise, although this was not the true equivalence point. Excellent results were obtained, the accuracy being 1–2%.

Procedure for blood serum. Measure, with a micrometer syringe, 0·2 ml of serum into a centrifuge tube. Add 0·2 ml of trichloroacetic acid solution (20% w/v) and centrifuge. Transfer 0·2 ml of the clear centrifugate to another tube and add 0·1 ml of sodium acetate solution (20% w/v) and 0·1 ml of sodium tetraphenylborate solution (0·5% w/v). Prepare a blank with 0·1 ml of water, 0·1 ml of trichloroacetic acid solution, sodium acetate and sodium tetraphenylborate solutions. Allow the tubes to stand for 20 min, then pipette 0·2 ml from each into separate cells suitable for a spectrophotometric titration. Add 10 ml of water to each cell. Place the cell containing the solution of unknown tetraphenylborate content in the spectrophotometer, and set the wavelength to 570 mμ and the optical density to zero. Titrate the solution with cetyltrimethylammonium bromide solution (0·075% w/v) from an Agla micrometer burette, measuring the optical density of the solution after each addition of 0·01 ml. Obtain the end-point from the usual plot. Titrate the blank solution in the same manner and subtract the first titre from the second to obtain the volume of standard cetylammonium bromide solution equivalent to the potassium content of the first solution.

6.9 Selenium. A few milligrams of selenium, present as selenite, have been determined by photometric titration with 0·01 M potassium iodide solution[231]. The maximum error was about 1%. The solution was 5–7 N in hydrochloric acid, and gum arabic was added as a protective colloid. Iodine and colloidal selenium were formed during the titration.

6.10 Silver. The concentration of silver in a solution can be determined by titrating turbidimetrically, a standard solution of thioacetamide (0·001–0·1 M) with the silver solution[232]. The method can be used for 50–1000 μg of silver. Results agree within 0·5% for 0·1 M solutions and 3% for 0·001 M.

6.11 Sulphate. Frey[233] has titrated sulphate (about 2 mg in about 100 ml of solution) to maximum turbidity with 0·02 N barium chloride solution with the help of a photometer. The solution contained 40% by volume of ethyl alcohol and was titrated at about 50°C. The average error was ± 5%. Total sulphur in vulcanised rubber was rapidly determined by such a titration.

Microgram amounts of sulphate have been determined by turbidimetric titration with standard barium chloride solution (approx. 0·0016 M)[159]. The solution to be titrated (33 ml) contained 90% (v/v) methanol, approximately 10 mg of sodium chloride, 60 mg of magnesium chloride hexahydrate and 10·5 mg of ammonium chloride. Titrations were performed using a filter photometer, and the end-point was located from a plot of relative optical density against volume of titrant added. The maximum error was 11% for 9–40 μg amounts of sulphate and 2% for 40–600 μg quantities. The method has been employed for the determination of trace amounts of sulphur in organic compounds.

Zimmermann[234] has modified the turbidimetric titration method of Wickbold[159], to increase the sensitivity 200-fold. The volume of solution titrated was reduced to 0·33 or 0·16 ml. 0·5 μg of sulphur as sulphate could be titrated and allowed 0·2 p.p.m. of sulphur in a few litres of air to be determined.

Van Nieuwenburg and Engelbert van Bevervoorde[235] have also examined the possibility of determining sulphate, using a turbidimetric titration with barium nitrate solution. They constructed their own simple photometer and determined the end-points from plots of galvanometer reading (relative transmission) against volume of titrant added. The reproducibility for the determination of 10 mg amounts of sulphate (as potassium sulphate) in about 30 ml of solution, was ± 1%. A mixture of 2 parts of water, 1 part of ethanol and 1 part of n-butanol was the most satisfactory medium for the titration of 2–20 mg of sulphate. The presence of equimolar amounts of alkali metal or ammonium chlorides caused the results to be low (by about 5%).

A recent study on the shapes of turbidimetric titration curves for the titration of potassium sulphate solution with barium chloride solution in the presence of various concentrations of ethyl alcohol has also been made by Miura and Nagakane[236].

6.12 Zinc. Frey[237] determined 10–35 mg of zinc oxide in 100 ml of solution with a maximum error of 5% by photometric titration with potassium ferrocyanide solution.

The application of type A turbidimetric titration to a few miscellaneous systems is now described.

6.13 Colloidal electrolytes. Lambert[238] has determined the concentration in dilute solutions of many surface active agents in the class of colloidal electrolytes, by turbidimetric titration. The method consisted of titrating an anionic agent with a cationic agent under such conditions that a colloidal precipitate was produced near the equivalence point, and was solubilized or coagulated with a small excess of reagent. The end-point was determined from a plot of optical density against volume of titrant added. A typical turbidity titration curve is shown in Fig. 22 where 40 ml of aqueous Igepon TD solution (about 0·001 N based on the active material, sodium N-oleyl-N-methyl-taurate) were titrated with 5×10^{-3} N aqueous cetyl pyridinium chloride solution. The solutions tested had concentrations of 0·05–2·0 g/l. and the accuracy was about ± 5% of the amount present. Any photometer, and presumably spectrophotometer, could be used for these titrations.

6.14 Nicotine. Goodhue[239] has determined small amounts of nicotine using a turbidimetric titration. A suitable volume of silicotungstic acid solution along with a few drops of solutions of formic acid and Irish moss extract were added to 0·05 to 0·75 mg of nicotine in the titration cell of a home-made photometer. Irish moss extract was used to stabilize the nicotine silicotungstate as a colloidal precipitate. The excess of silicotungstic acid was determined by titration to maximum turbidity with standard nicotine formate solution. The quantity of standard nicotine formate solution, equivalent to the silicotungstic acid added, was determined by a blank titration. The maximum error was ± 9 μg.

6.15 Polymers. Turbidimetric titrations have also been employed for the qualitative examination of polymers and to determine molecular weight distributions in polymers[240, 241, 242, 243, 244, 245].

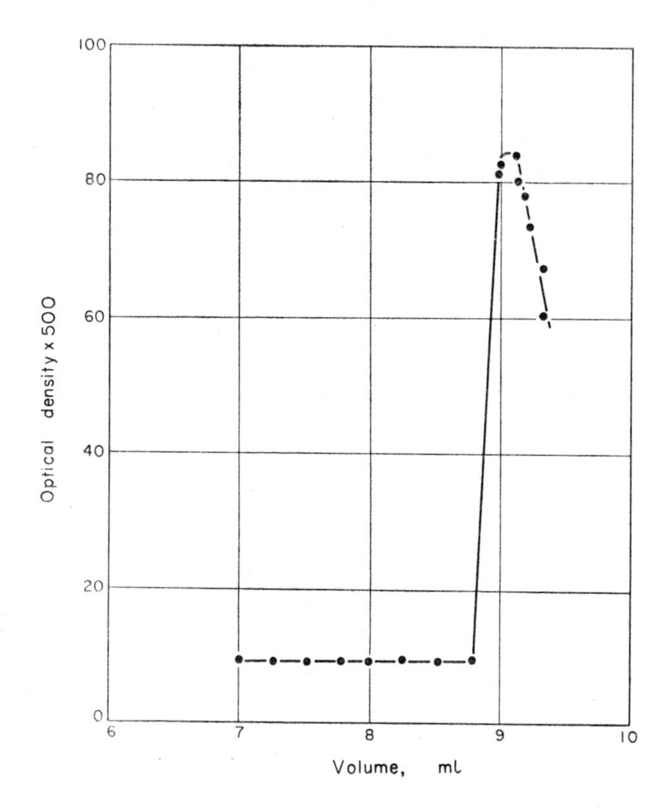

FIG. 22. Titration of 40 ml of Igepon TD solution (about 10^{-3} N based on the active material, sodium N-oleyl-N-methyl-taurate) with 5×10^{-3} N aqueous cetyl pyridinium chloride solution

6.16 Protein. Kibardin and Davydova[246] have identified certain blood serum proteins from the shape of the titration curves obtained by plotting optical density against volume of titrant added, for the titration of serum in solutions buffered to pH 8·7 (acetate–barbiturate) with cupric or zinc sulphate solutions.

Type B titrations

6.17 Fluoride. Nichols and Kindt[247], using a home-made instrument, showed that photometric end-point detection could be profitably applied to the determination of milligram quantities of fluoride by titration with thorium nitrate solution using sodium alizarin sulphonate as indicator. Improvements on their method made during the last decade are discussed below.

A filter photometer was employed by Mavrodineanu and Gwirtsman[248] to detect the end-point in the titration of microgram quantities of fluoride with the titrant and indicator used by Nichols and Kindt[247]. Titration of fluoride in 250 ml of solution of pH 3·0 ± 0·05 was made at 520 mμ. The end-point was assumed to have been reached when the galvanometer spot of the instrument had been deflected a set distance from its initial position. It was necessary to subtract the titre obtained for a fluoride-free blank from those of the fluoride solutions to obtain the volume of standard thorium nitrate solution equivalent to the titrated fluoride. A plot of optical density against volume of titrant added would give the end-point without the use of a blank titration.

Ma and Gwirtsman[249] applied the same photometric titration to the microdetermination of fluorine in organic compounds. These organic fluoro-compounds were decomposed by sodium fusion in a Parr microbomb, and the fluoride separated from interfering elements by steam distillation.

The same means of end-point determination was also employed for the determination of fluoride in plant tissue, air and water[250]. When necessary, the fluoride was separated from elements which would interfere in the subsequent titration, by distillation as fluosilicic acid.

The method of end-point detection used by Gwirtsman *et al.*[250] has since been applied to the determination of fluorine in catalysts[251]. The fluorine was determined by volatilizing fluosilicic acid, in a stream of oxygen, from the sample which was being heated in an induction furnace. The fluosilicic acid was absorbed in dilute sodium hydroxide solution.

Lee *et al.*[53] employed a spectrophotometric titration for the determination of fluorine in radioactive samples after a pyrohydrolytic separation. The titration was carried out at 525 mμ with the usual titrant and indicator, namely thorium nitrate and sodium alizarin sulphonate.

Menis *et al.*[48] have determined 5–50 μg of fluoride in 35 ml of solution buffered at pH 3·0 with chloroacetate, by automatic spectrophotometric titration with 0·0005 M thorium nitrate solution, again using sodium alizarin sulphonate as indicator. The end-point was obtained from the recorded plot of optical density at 520 mμ against volume of titrant added. The method was accurate to within 1 μg of the actual fluoride content.

Newman[252] has also employed a similar photometric titration of fluoride for its determination in rock phosphates. Fluoride was separated from phosphate and interfering cations by adding alkaline EDTA solution to a hydrochloric acid solution of the rock, and passing a suitable aliquot of the resulting solution through a column of a strongly basic anion exchange resin in the chloride form. On eluting with an ammonia–ammonium chloride solution, the fluoride was removed from the column while phosphate and EDTA complexes of interfering metals were retained.

Dean *et al.*[253] have compared visual and spectrophotometric titrations for the determination of fluoride. Thorium nitrate was again the titrant and sodium alizarin sulphonate the indicator. The spectrophotometric titrations were made at 540 mμ and were suitable for concentrations of fluoride up to 150 p.p.m. These workers concluded that there was no significant difference between the results for spectrophotometric titrations and for visual titrations made by an experienced operator. However, for those laboratories where fluoride titrations are only performed occasionally a spectrophotometric titration is to be preferred, because good results are only obtained by visual titrations after considerable experience with the colour change at the end-point.

Hollingworth[160] has used a spectrophotometric titration for the determination of fluoride in rocks. A quantitative isolation of fluorine was obtained by a sodium peroxide decomposition, followed by a precipitation of silica and alumina, and a steam distillation of the filtrates. A suitable aliquot of the distillate adjusted to pH 3·05–3·10 was titrated spectrophotometrically with thorium nitrate solution using SPADNS (sodium salt of 2-(*p*-sulphophenylazo)-1,8-dihydroxy-naphthalene-3,6-disulphonic acid) as indicator. The method was capable of determining fluorine to within 4 μg for

0·25 g samples of rock. There seems to be no reason why the titration should not be applied to any solution containing fluoride, isolated if necessary, by distillation.

Procedure for titration. Transfer to a suitable titration cell, 25 ml of fluoride solution (containing ≯ 70 μg fluorine) whose pH has been adjusted to 3·05–3·10 by the addition of sodium hydroxide or hydrochloric acid solutions. Add 0·5 ml of aqueous indicator solution (0·02% w/v). Set the wavelength to 580 mμ, start the stirrer in motion and adjust the optical density reading to zero. Titrate the solution with standard thorium nitrate solution (about 0·001 M) adding the titrant in 0·05 ml increments. Locate the end-point from a plot of optical density against volume of titrant added. The thorium nitrate solution must be standardized using known amounts of sodium fluoride carried through the distillation process.

6.18 Fluosilicate. Fluosilicate in chromium plating baths was determined by photometric titration with thorium nitrate solution, using ferric salicylate as indicator[254]. 2–12 mg of fluosilicate in about 20 ml of solution buffered at pH 2·8 (chloroacetate) and containing ferric salicylate and the surfactant, polyoxyethylene sorbitan laurate, were titrated photometrically with 0·25 M thorium nitrate solution. The optical density of the solution, due to ferric salicylate, reached a maximum at the end-point after which it remained steady. (Before the end-point part of the iron was complexed by fluoride.) The error in the method was less than 2%

6.19 Sulphate. Menis and co-workers[48] have determined 6–50 μg of sulphate by automatic spectrophotometric titration at 520 mμ, with 0·00125 M barium perchlorate solution using thoron (2-2(hydroxy-3,6-disulpho-1-naphthylazo)-benzene arsonic acid) as indicator. The coefficient of variation in the results was about 5%.

CHAPTER 7

COULOMETRIC TITRATIONS WITH PHOTOMETRIC END-POINTS

These may equally well be termed photometric titrations with electrically generated titrant. It is obvious that visual end-point detection in the coulometric titration of microgram quantities of material would often be unreliable, and spectrophotometric end-point detection is one way of determining the exact equivalence point for such systems. Only a few of these titrations have been carried out, but they have been found useful where potentiometric or amperometric end-point detection is less reliable because of, for example, electrical coupling between the generating and indicating circuits.

Applications

7.1 Arsenic. Wise and co-workers[255], using an automatic coulometric titrator constructed in their laboratories, have titrated 0·2–1·0 m-equiv. of arsenic (III) in 150 ml of solution, 0·4–0·5 M in potassium iodide and 0·1–0·25 M in sodium dihydrogen phosphate with the pH adjusted to 6·4–7·0 by the addition of sodium hydroxide. The titrant was iodine produced by anodic oxidation in the stirred solution. A constant current of 50–175 mA between platinum foil electrodes was used. The optical system consisted of a light bulb and phototube detector. No filter was necessary. A trace of excess of iodine in the solution caused a relay to operate and the titration was terminated. The error in a series of titrations at no time exceeded 0·25%.

A similar method has been used by Everett and Reilley[256] for the coulometric titration of microgram quantities of arsenite. These workers performed the titrations in plastic cells which fitted into the cell compartment of a Beckman B spectrophotometer. A simple electrical circuit was used to produce constant current in the range 0·001 to 7 mA. With 10–50 μg of arsenic the error ranged from 1 to 2·5%, and with 50–100 μg from 0 to 1%.

Procedure. To a cell of approximately 25 ml capacity, add 5 ml of 0·3 N potassium iodide solution and 10 ml of 0·5 M sodium bicarbonate solution to buffer the solution to about pH 8·3. Add a small quantity of standard arsenite solution to the cell and select a constant current suitable for the subsequent titration of the solution of unknown arsenic content. Select a wavelength of 342 mμ, adjust the optical density scale reading to zero, set the stirrer in motion and allow the coulometric titration to proceed until the optical density starts to increase. Then take four or five readings at intervals of a few seconds. This preliminary titration after the addition of a little arsenite is necessary because the 0·3 N iodide solution usually contains a trace of iodine. Now add a suitable quantity of the solution whose arsenite content is to be determined. This should contain 10–100 μg of arsenic. The optical density falls to zero. Titrate the arsenite in the cell as before.

Plot optical density against time and determine from the graph the time of passage of the constant current for the quantity of arsenite solution added. A typical plot is shown in Fig. 23.

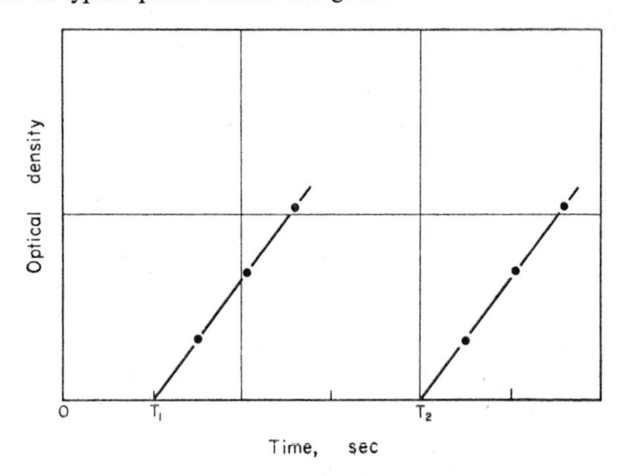

FIG. 23. The type of plots obtained in the titration of 25–100 μg of arsenic (as arsenite) with electrically generated iodine at 342 mμ. T_1 is the time required to titrate the small amount of arsenite added to the iodide solution before the sample (the blank titration). $T_2 - T_1$ is the time required to titrate the arsenite in the sample itself. (By courtesy of *Analytical Chemistry*)

Arsenic (III) may also be titrated spectrophotometrically with electrically generated cerium (IV). Furman and Fenton[257] determined 50–1000 μg of arsenic in this way with a maximum error of 2·7% for 50–150 μg and of 0·5% for 150–1000 μg. The titrations were carried out in a special cell which fitted into the cell compartment of a Beckman DU spectrophotometer. Generating currents of 0·4–5 mA were employed, and anodic oxidations occurred at a platinum–iridium foil electrode in a saturated solution of cerous sulphate, 1 N with respect to sulphuric acid. It was necessary to add to the solution a trace of osmium tetroxide to catalyse the otherwise slow oxidation of arsenite. Spectrophotometric end-point detection was made at 320, 360 or 370 mμ depending on the current level. The solution did not absorb until an excess of ceric ion was present. The end-point was determined from a plot of optical density against time in the usual manner.

7.2 Iron. Malmstadt and Roberts[258] have determined iron in titanium sponge, alloys and ores by automatic coulometric titration with spectrophotometric end-point detection. A sample of material is dissolved with sulphuric or sulphuric–fluoboric acid mixture, and the iron is oxidized fully to the trivalent state with potassium permanganate, excess permanganate being reduced with sodium azide, which itself is destroyed by boiling. A small volume of dilute leucomethylene blue solution is added to the hot solution and the beaker placed in the cell compartment of an automatic derivative spectrophotometric titrator[36]. The titrant, titanous ion, was produced by cathodic reduction at a constant current of 50 or 70 mA at a pre-treated platinum gauze electrode. A wavelength of 665 mμ was used. As the end-point was approached the optical density of the dark blue solution decreased sharply to become almost constant after the end-point, when the indicator was present in the reduced, colourless state. A plot of optical density against milliequivalents of titrant gave a very sharp inflection point at the end-point and the titration was therefore terminated automatically by the second derivative technique[36].

By this method samples containing 0·01–20% of iron may be analysed with an average error of about 0·003%. Only copper, molybdenum and vanadium interfere.

7.3 Titanium. The method of section 7.2 has been adapted for the determination of titanium in sponge and ores[259]. A suitable aliquot of the solution of the sample was passed through a cadmium reductor to reduce the titanium completely to the titanous state. The effluent from the reductor was collected under 50 ml of standard ferric solution in a titration cell. In this way the titanium (III) was oxidized to titanium (IV) and an equivalent amount of iron (III) was reduced to iron (II). The iron (III) remaining was determined by automatic derivative spectrophotometric titration with electrically generated titanium (III). The precision and accuracy of the determinations were within about 0·1%.

7.4 Vanadium. Malmstadt and Roberts[260] have determined traces of vanadium in titanium tetrachloride by automatic spectrophotometric titration with electrically generated titanous ion. A 10 ml sample of titanium tetrachloride was hydrolysed in hydrochloric acid solution and the resulting solution, 7·5 M with respect to hydrochloric acid, contained vanadium in the +4 and +5 oxidation states. The solution was transferred directly to the titration vessel, which fitted into the cell compartment of a Cary spectrophotometer. Titanous ions were generated by cathodic reductions at either a titanium metal rod or platinum foil electrode at a constant current of approximately 57 mA. At either 490 or 760 mμ a plot of optical density against time was recorded automatically. Breaks occurred in the plot when all of the vanadium (V) had been reduced to vanadium (IV), and when all of the vanadium (IV) was reduced to vanadium (III). The distance between the first and second breaks was a measure of the time required for the complete reduction of the vanadium (IV) to vanadium (III) and hence of the amount of vanadium in the solution. The percentage of vanadium in the titanium tetrachloride samples was determined in the usual manner, using Faraday's Law.

Samples containing 0·01–0·2% of vanadium were analysed with an average error of about 0·00016%.

7.5 Acids and bases. By use of the instrument mentioned in 7.1, Wise and co-workers[255] have shown that automatic photometric titrations with electrically generated hydroxyl ion may be employed for the determination of acids using one-colour or two-colour indicators. They tested the feasibility of the method using a standard solution of potassium hydrogen phthalate and a special titration cell. The electrodes were platinum foil, the electrolyte 0·5 M sodium sulphate and the generating current about 50 mA. Phenolphthalein was used as one-colour indicator in conjunction with a deep green filter to increase the sensitivity of detection of the end-point. The two-colour indicator was thymol blue used with a yellow filter. In both these cases, the optical density of the solution increased rapidly at the end-point, but premature end-points were obtained because of bubbles of hydrogen which formed in the solution. Both the effect of bubbles in the solution and a darkening of the colour of the solution increased the optical density and produced a similar photocell response. However, these bubbles soon escaped from the solution and the addition of titrant was restarted until the end-point was obtained.

0·17–0·28 m-equiv. of potassium hydrogen phthalate were determined by the above method with a maximum error of 0·11% using a one-colour indicator. With a two-colour indicator, 0·12–0·27 m-equiv. of the same substance were determined with a maximum error of 0·16%.

The trouble with bubbles in the solution has been overcome by these workers using a ratio-detecting attachment for the automatic titrator[261].

Automatic photometric titration with electrically generated titrant has been applied by Liberti[262] to the detection and determination of organic acids and bases, after their separation by gas phase chromatography. The vapours on emerging from the chromatographic column were absorbed into a solution of 0·5 M sodium sulphate, containing a suitable indicator, in a Perspex cell. A differential photometric system, unaffected by changes of optical density caused by bubbles originating on the generating electrode, was employed. When, for example, an acid gas was present in the gas stream, it caused the pH of the solution to fall. The optical density of the solution changed and a relay operated to start the coulometric titration. In this case, hydroxyl ions were generated at the cathode at a steady rate, and soon returned the pH of the solution and the optical density reading to their original values, whence a relay operated to terminate the titration. A similar system was used for the detection of bases. The original paper should be consulted for more details.

7.6 Olefins. Miller and DeFord[263] have determined the bromine number of 3·4–11 mg samples of olefins with a precision of better than 2%, using a spectrophotometric titration with electrically generated bromine. The titrations were performed in a 100 ml beaker which fitted into the cell compartment of a Cary recording spectrophotometer. The anode, at which the bromine was generated, was a platinum foil electrode. The constant current of 50 mA was supplied by a commercial instrument.

The solvent in the anodic compartment consisted of glacial acetic acid–methanol (3 : 1) with a small amount of potassium bromide and hydrochloric acid added. Mercuric chloride was used as catalyst. Titrations were performed at 360 mμ where the free bromine absorbs. The end-points in the titrations were obtained from recorded plots of optical density against time. With certain olefins, where reaction was incomplete at the end-point, roundness occurred in the vicinity of the end-point, but this was readily determined by extrapolation.

7.7 Dyestuffs. Munemori[264] has titrated photometrically the dyestuffs methylene blue and indigo carmine with electrically generated dithionite. Dithionite ions were produced with 100% current efficiency at a mercury-pool cathode, the cathodic compartment of the cell containing 0·01 M sodium bisulphite buffered at pH 3–5. 2–6 mg of dyestuff were titrated in about 50 ml of solution. The end-point was obtained from a plot of optical density against time for a wavelength of 610 mμ.

CHAPTER 8

MISCELLANEOUS APPLICATIONS

A few photometric titrations which do not readily fit into the other chapters are discussed here.

8.1 Water. Bruckenstein[265] has determined water in glacial acetic acid by spectrophotometric titration at 256 mμ with acetic anhydride, in the presence of sulphuric acid as a catalyst. Acetic anhydride absorbs appreciably at 256 mμ while water, acetic acid and sulphuric acid scarcely absorb at that wavelength. Water in the concentration range of 0·009 to 1·7 % was satisfactorily determined, the maximum error for amounts in excess of 1 % being 0·1 %, for amounts between 0·1 and 1 %, 0·004 %, and for amounts less than 0·1 %, 0·0006 %.

Procedure. Transfer about 3 ml of the acetic acid sample to a weighed 1 cm square silica cell in a dry box. Remove the stoppered cell from the dry box, weigh it and replace it in the dry box. Add 0·1 ml of water-free 2 M sulphuric acid in acetic acid. Place the cell in a spectrophotometer, set the wavelength to 256 mμ and the optical density reading to zero. Return the cell to the dry box and add a suitable volume of acetic anhydride from a 0·1 or 0·01 ml ultramicroburette. Measure the optical density of the solution and carry on in this manner until about six optical density readings after the equivalence point have been obtained. Locate the end-point from a plot of optical density against volume of titrant added.

8.2 Critical micelle concentrations of soap solutions. Nichols and Kindt[247] have used a photometric titration for the determination of the critical concentration for the formation of micelles in soap solutions. Above the critical micelle concentration, the absorption spectrum of a dye in soap solution is characteristic of its solutions in organic solvents, while below the critical micelle concentration the dye has an entirely different absorption spectrum. The above workers determined critical micelle concentrations for cationic and anionic soaps by preparing a soap solution, 10^{-5} M with respect to a dye, and titrating it photometrically with a 10^{-5} M aqueous dye solution. To test the method they used sodium dodecyl sulphate with pinacyanol chloride solution, and n-decyl and n-dodecyl trimethyl ammonium bromides with Sky Blue FF solution. They employed a home-made filter photometer and took the end-point (the critical micelle concentration) as the point at which a maximum change in transmission of the solution occurred. Better end-point location would be obtained by plotting optical density readings against volume of titrant added, and the method described below applies to a spectrophotometric titration with end-point location in this manner.

Procedure. Dissolve a weighed sample of an anionic soap (1·9 g with sodium dodecyl sulphate) in a litre of 10^{-5} M aqueous pinacyanol chloride solution, so that the concentration of the soap in the solution is above the critical micelle concentration. Add 65 ml of this solution to a suitable titration cell. Set the stirrer in motion, select a wavelength of 610 mμ and adjust the optical density reading to a suitable high value. Titrate the solution with 10^{-5} M pinacyanol solution added in 0·5 ml increments and record the optical density readings after 2 min intervals. When the optical density readings stop falling, record only a few more readings. Obtain the end-point from a plot of optical density against volume of titrant added, and calculate the critical micelle concentration for the soap in question.

If a cationic soap is being titrated with Sky Blue as indicator, use a wavelength of 625 mμ.

8.3 Photonometric determination of vanadium and chromium. Bricker and Schonberg[40] have determined these elements by a most interesting method. They were able to produce iron (II) for the reduction of vanadium (V) or chromium (VI) by the photolysis of a solution containing iron (III), oxalic acid and sulphuric acid using radiation from a mercury-vapour lamp. The iron (II) reacted immediately with vanadium (V) or chromium (VI), to reduce them to vanadium (IV) or chromium (III) respectively. Radiation from the lamp generated titrant at a constant rate, because the quantum efficiency of the reductions remained essentially constant over a wide range of experimental conditions. The end-points were determined spectrophotometrically. Vanadium (IV) absorbs appreciably at 750 mμ and this wavelength is suitable when vanadium (V) is being titrated. With chromium (VI) a wavelength of 575 mμ, where chromium (III) absorbs, is employed. 1·4–70 mg of vanadium (V) in 125 ml of solution were determined with an average error of $\pm$ 1·5%, and 8–52 mg of chromium (VI) in the same volume with an average error of ± 3%. The original paper should be consulted for more details.

8.4 Procaine, propoxycaine and tetracaine hydrochlorides. These compounds in 6 N hydrochloric acid solution have been determined by spectrophotometric titration with 0·1 M sodium nitrite solution[266]. In these titrations, nitrous acid is first produced and then reacts with the primary aromatic amines, procaine hydrochloride and propoxycaine hydrochloride, to give the expected diazonium chloride. It was found that, at 385 mμ, little or no absorption occurred with procaine mono- and dihydrochlorides, procaine diazonium chloride, and propoxycaine mono- and dihydrochlorides. However, both propoxycaine diazonium chloride and excess of nitrous acid absorb appreciably at this wavelength. Hence in the spectrophotometric titration of procaine hydrochloride the optical density readings scarcely changed up to the equivalence point, but increased rapidly as the concentration of free nitrous acid steadily increased after the end-point.

With propoxycaine hydrochloride, the diazonium chloride absorbs much more strongly than nitrous acid, and so the plot of optical density against volume of titrant added consists of a steeply rising line to the equivalence point, followed by a line of only slight gradient after the end-point. Tetracaine hydrochloride being a secondary amine reacts with nitrous acid to form a nitroso derivative. Tetracaine dihydrochloride does not absorb at 385 mμ, but both the tetracaine nitroso derivative and nitrous acid do, the former more so than the latter. Hence, in the spectrophotometric titration of tetracaine hydrochloride, the plot of optical density against volume of titrant added consisted of a fairly steep line to the equivalence point, followed by a less steep line after the end-point.

410–450 mg amounts of procaine hydrochloride were determined with a maximum error of 0·4%. 1·5 mg amounts of propoxycaine hydrochloride and 30 mg amounts of tetracaine hydrochloride were determined with maximum errors of 0·35% and 1% respectively.

Procedure (for procaine hydrochloride). Add the sample containing 100–500 mg of procaine hydrochloride to a suitable titration cell and dilute to 150 ml with 6 N hydrochloric acid solution. Set the wavelength to 385 mμ, start the stirrer into motion and adjust the optical density reading to zero. Titrate in the usual manner with standard 0·1 M sodium nitrite solution, taking optical density readings after each addition of titrant. Locate the end-point from a plot of optical density readings corrected for volume change, against volume of titrant added.

8.5 Addition and substitution reactions with bromine. Sweetser and Bricker[16] have employed spectrophotometric titration for the determination of the bromine numbers of unsaturated compounds, and for the determination of organic compounds which undergo substitution reactions with bromine. The titrant was in all cases a mixture of potassium bromate and potassium bromide, which react in the presence of hydrogen ions and more potassium bromide to produce the tribromide ion. The tribromide ion absorbs strongly in the ultra-violet region of the spectrum; hence excess of bromine (as tribromide) in the solution is easily detected if a suitable wavelength below 360 mμ is chosen. The optimum wavelength for a particular titration depends on the concentration of the titrant and varies from 270 mμ for 0·001 N titrant to 360 mμ for 0·25 N reagent. If the reaction product formed in the titration does not absorb at the chosen wavelength, then the plot of optical density against volume of titrant added consists of a horizontal straight line to the end-point followed by a steeply rising line after the equivalence point.

Milligram amounts of the following unsaturated compounds were satisfactorily titrated with bromine, namely, 10-hendecenoic acid, oleic acid, 1-octene, allyl alcohol, 3-phenyl-4-nitro-cyclohexene and cholesteryl acetate. An average deviation from the mean of about 0·3% was obtained for the titrations of these compounds. In order to increase the rate of addition of bromine in some of the slower bromination reactions, mercuric chloride or zinc sulphate was added as a catalyst.

Procedure for the determination of oleic acid. Add to a suitable titration cell 50 ml of glacial acetic acid, 20 ml of methanol, 1·2 ml of concentrated hydrochloric acid, 2 ml of 40% potassium bromide solution and a known volume of solution containing 0·14–0·24 g of oleic acid. Start the stirrer into motion, set the wavelength to 360 mμ and adjust the optical density reading to zero. Titrate the solution with 0·25 N potassium bromate–potassium bromide solution (M/24 potassium bromate + 5/24 M potassium bromide) until the optical density reading starts to rise. Then add small aliquots of titrant and record the optical density readings 1 min after each addition. Locate the end-point graphically in the usual way and calculate the bromine number.

Organic compounds which undergo substitution reactions with bromine were also determined by a similar titration. These compounds fall into three groups, namely, (1) those compounds which have moderate to fast rates of bromination and are insensitive to excess of bromine, (2) those compounds which have moderate to fast rates of bromination and are sensitive to excess of bromine, and (3) those compounds which show a slow rate of bromination and are insensitive to excess of bromine.

Aniline, a compound in the first category, was determined to within 0·2% by a procedure similar to that described for oleic acid, except that the solvent (100 ml) was methanol–water–12 N hydrochloric acid–40% potassium bromide solution (30 : 40 : 3 : 2 v/v).

o-Cresol, a compound in the second category, was determined to within 0·2% by carrying out a similar titration at 300 mμ. At this wavelength the instrument is very sensitive for tribromide ion, therefore the excess of bromine in the solution after the equivalence point is kept at a minimum.

Finally, phenol, a compound in the third category, was satisfactorily determined by a modified procedure in which a fixed amount of tribromide ion was, in effect, present at the start of the titration, and again after the addition of a volume of bromate–bromide solution equivalent to the phenol. The original paper should be consulted for full details.

REFERENCES

1 R. H. Osborn, J. H. Elliot and A. F. Martin, *Industr. Engng. Chem. (Anal.)*, **15**, 642 (1943).
2 W. J. Lane and J. S. Fritz, *U.S. Atomic Energy Comm. Rep.* ISC-945 (1957).
3 R. H. Müller and H. M. Partridge, *Industr. Engng. Chem.*, **20**, 423 (1928).
4 R. H. Müller and M. H. McKenna, *J. Amer. Chem. Soc.*, **58**, 1017 (1936).
5 J. C. Hindeman, L. B. Magnusson and T. J. LaChapelle, *J. Amer. Chem. Soc.*, **71**, 687 (1949).
6 R. F. Goddu and D. N. Hume, *Analyt. Chem.*, **26**, 1740 (1954).
7 A. L. Underwood, *J. Chem. Educ.*, **31**, 394 (1954).
8 J. B. Headridge, *Talanta*, **1**, 293 (1958).
9 S. Musha and K. Ogawa, *Japan Analyst*, **6**, 849 (1957).
10 M. Bobtelsky, *Heterometry*, Elsevier, Amsterdam, 1960.
11 J. Zyka, *Chemie*, **10**, 539 (1958).
12 C. E. Bricker and L. J. Loeffler, *Analyt. Chem.*, **27**, 1419 (1955).
13 K. J. Karrman, E. Bladh and P.-O. Gedda, *Mikrochim. Acta*, 779 (1959).
14 C. N. Reilley and B. Schweizer, *Analyt. Chem.*, **26**, 1124 (1954).
15 C. E. Bricker and P. B. Sweetser, *Analyt. Chem.*, **25**, 764 (1953).
16 P. B. Sweetser and C. E. Bricker, *Analyt. Chem.*, **24**, 1107 (1952).
17 M. Bobtelsky, *Heterometry*, Elsevier, Amsterdam, 1960, p. 42.
18 E. Grunwald, *Analyt. Chem.*, **28**, 1112 (1956).
19 J. A. Hunter and C. C. Miller, *Analyst*, **81**, 79 (1956).
20 P. B. Sweetser and C. E. Bricker, *Analyt. Chem.*, **25**, 253 (1953).
21 P. W. West and C. G. de Vries, *Analyt. Chem.*, **23**, 334 (1951).
22 P. W. West and E. S. Amis, *Industr. Engng. Chem. (Anal.)*, **18**, 400 (1946).
23 E. B. Sandell, *Colorimetric Determination of Traces of Metals*, 3rd Ed., Interscience, New York, 1959, p. 101.
24 R. F. Goddu and D. N. Hume, *Analyt. Chem.*, **26**, 1679 (1954).
25 T. Higuchi, C. Rehm and C. Barnstein, *Analyt. Chem.*, **28**, 1506 (1956).
26 C. Rehm and T. Higuchi, *Analyt. Chem.*, **29**, 367 (1957).
27 J. I. Bodin, *Thesis*, University of Wisconsin, 1958.
28 K. A. Connors and T. Higuchi, *Analyt. Chem.*, **32**, 93 (1960).
29 J. M. H. Fortuin, P. Karsten and H. L. Kies, *Analyt. Chim. Acta*, **10**, 356 (1954).
30 H. Flaschka and S. Khalafalla, *Z. analyt. Chem.*, **156**, 401 (1957).
31 G. Schwarzenbach, *Complexometric Titrations* (translated by H. Irving), Methuen, London, 1957, pp. 63, 66 and 72.
32 A. Ringbom and E. Vänninen, *Analyt. Chim. Acta*, **11**, 153 (1954).
33 C. N. Reilley and R. W. Schmid, *Analyt. Chem.*, **31**, 887 (1959).
34 J. M. Thorburn, C. M. Jankowski and M. S. Reynolds, *Analyt. Chem.*, **31**, 124 (1959).
35 E. H. Sargent & Co., *Scientific Apparatus and Methods*, **10**, No. 2, p. 1 (1958).
36 H. V. Malmstadt and C. B. Roberts, *Analyt. Chem.*, **28**, 1408 (1956).

37 H. V. Malmstadt and D. A. Vassallo, *Analyt. Chim. Acta*, **16**, 455 (1957).
38 G. J. Krasl and G. P. McFaul, *U.S. Pat.* 2812242 (Nov. 5th, 1957).
39 J. B. Headridge and R. J. Magee, *Talanta*, **1**, 117, 416 (1958).
40 C. E. Bricker and S. S. Schonberg, *Analyt. Chem.*, **30**, 922 (1958).
41 R. F. Goddu and D. N. Hume, *Analyt. Chem.*, **22**, 1314 (1950).
42 C. E. Bricker and P. B. Sweetser, *Analyt. Chem.*, **24**, 409 (1952).
43 D. W. Klingman, D. T. Hooker and C. V. Banks, *Analyt. Chem.*, **27**, 572 (1955).
44 J. Herrington, *Unicam Spectrovision*, (6), 5 (1958).
45 G. W. C. Milner and J. W. Edwards, *Analyst*, **80**, 879 (1955).
46 H. V. Malmstadt and E. C. Gohrbrandt, *Analyt. Chem.*, **26**, 442 (1954).
47 T. L. Marple and D. N. Hume, *Analyt. Chem.*, **28**, 1116 (1956).
48 O. Menis, D. L. Manning and R. G. Ball, *Analyt. Chem.*, **30**, 1772 (1958).
49 P. W. Mullen and A. Anton, *Analyt. Chem.*, **32**, 103 (1960).
50 R. A. Chalmers and C. A. Walley, *Analyst*, **82**, 329 (1957).
51 J. P. Phillips, *Automatic Titrators*, Academic Press, New York, 1959.
52 D. J. Fricker, *Chem. & Ind.*, 426 (1955).
53 J. E. Lee, J. H. Edgerton and M. T. Kelley, *Analyt. Chem.*, **28**, 1441 (1956).
54 C. Rehm, J. I. Bodin, K. A. Connors and T. Higuchi, *Analyt. Chem.*, **31**, 483 (1959).
55 T. R. Sweet and J. Zehner, *Analyt. Chem.*, **30**, 1713 (1958).
56 M. Bobtelsky, *Heterometry*, Elsevier, Amsterdam, 1960, p. 22.
57 L. Shapiro and W. W. Brannock, *Analyt. Chem.*, **27**, 725 (1955).
58 K. Y. Bril, S. Holzer and B. Rethy, *Analyt. Chem.*, **31**, 1353 (1959).
59 J. P. Phillips, *J. Chem. Educ.*, **34**, 203 (1957).
60 D. N. Sunderman and R. C. Propst, *U.S. Atomic Energy Comm.*, DP-SPU 53–8 (1953).
61 J. W. Loveland, R. W. Adams, H. H. King, F. A. Nowak and L. J. Cali, *Analyt. Chem.*, **31**, 1008 (1959).
62 G. W. Leonard and R. W. Henry, *Analyt. Chem.*, **28**, 1079 (1956).
63 R. W. McKinney and C. A. Reynolds, *Talanta*, **1**, 46 (1958).
64 L. E. I. Hummelstedt and D. N. Hume, *Analyt. Chem.*, **32**, 576 (1960).
65 R. M. Powers, R. A. Day and A. L. Underwood, *Analyt. Chem.*, **30**, 254 (1958).
66 A. T. James and A. J. P. Martin, *Biochem. J.*, **50**, 679 (1952).
67 A. T. James, A. J. P. Martin and G. H. Smith, *Biochem. J.*, **52**, 238 (1952).
68 A. T. James and A. J. P. Martin, *Analyst*, **77**, 915 (1952).
69 H. V. Malmstadt and D. A. Vassallo, *Analyt. Chem.*, **31**, 206 (1959).
70 H. V. Malmstadt and D. A. Vassallo, *Analyt. Chem.*, **31**, 862 (1959).
71 W. J. Schuele, J. F. Hazel and W. M. McNabb, *Analyt. Chem.*, **28**, 505 (1956).
72 P. Karsten, H. L. Kies and P. de Hoog, *Rec. Trav. Chim. Pays-Bas*, **79**, 610 (1960).
73 T. Somiya and Y. Yasuda, *J. Soc. Chem. Ind. Japan*, **41**, Suppl. binding 314 (1938).
74 M. S. Gaukhman, B. E. Reznik and G. M. Ganzburg, *Zavodskaya Lab.*, **16**, 1031 (1950).
75 M. G. Bapat and S. V. Tatwawadi, *Naturwissenschaften*, **44**, 557 (1957).
76 G. F. Smith, *Cerate Oxidimetry*, G. F. Smith Publishing Co., Columbus, Ohio, 1942.

77 T. L. Marple, E. P. Pryzbylowicz and D. N. Hume, *Analyt. Chem.*, **28**, 1892 (1956).
78 J. W. Edwards and G. W. C. Milner, *Analyst*, **82**, 593 (1957).
79 J. W. Miles and D. T. Englis, *Analyt. Chem.*, **27**, 1996 (1955).
80 H. V. Malmstadt and T. P. Hadjiioannou, *Analyt. Chim. Acta*, **21**, 41 (1959).
81 S. Hirano, *J. Soc. Chem. Ind. Japan*, **37**, Suppl. binding 178 (1934).
82 S. Hirano, *J. Soc. Chem. Ind. Japan*, **37**, Suppl. binding 561 (1934).
83 G. S. Deshmukh and S. V. Tatwawadi, *Z. analyt. Chem.*, **168**, 411 (1959).
84 G. E. F. Lundell, J. I. Hoffman and H. A. Bright, *Chemical Analysis of Iron and Steel*, Wiley, New York, 1931.
85 V. F. Barkovskii, *Zhur. analit. Khim.*, **13**, 682 (1958).
86 S. V. Tatwawadi, *Z. analyt. Chem.*, **168**, 15 (1959).
87 C. J. B. Smit, M. A. Joslyn and A. Lukton, *Analyt. Chem.*, **27**, 1159 (1955).
88 V. Zitko, *Chem. Zvesti*, **12**, 533 (1958).
89 C. N. Reilley, R. W. Schmid and F. S. Sadek, *J. Chem. Educ.*, **36**, 555 (1959).
90 C. N. Reilley, R. W. Schmid and F. S. Sadek, *J. Chem. Educ.*, **36**, 619 (1959).
91 K. Rowley, R. W. Stoenner and L. Gordon, *Analyt. Chem.*, **28**, 136 (1956).
92 T. J. Manns, M. U. Reschovsky and A. J. Certa, *Analyt. Chem.*, **24**, 908 (1952).
93 A. I. Cohen and L. Gordon, *Analyt. Chem.*, **28**, 1445 (1956).
94 A. L. Underwood, *Analyt. Chem.*, **26**, 1322 (1954).
95 R. N. Wilhite and A. L. Underwood, *Analyt. Chem.*, **27**, 1334 (1955).
96 G. W. C. Milner and A. Bacon, *A.E.R.E. Report* C/R, 2494 (1958).
97 V. Suk and V. Miketukova, *Chem. Listy*, **52**, 2408 (1958).
98 P. B. Sweetser and C. E. Bricker, *Analyt. Chem.*, **26**, 195 (1954).
99 A. C. Kibrick, M. Ross and H. E. Rogers, *Proc. Soc. Exp. Biol., N.Y.*, **81**, 353 (1952).
100 F. W. Fales, *J. Biol. Chem.*, **204**, 577 (1953).
101 J. Lehmann, *Scand. J. Clin. Lab. Invest.*, **5**, 203 (1953).
102 R. A. Chalmers, *Analyst*, **79**, 519 (1954).
103 E. P. Clark and J. B. Collip, *J. Biol. Chem.*, **63**, 461 (1925).
104 B. Kramer and F. F. Tisdall, *J. Biol. Chem.*, **47**, 475 (1921).
105 L. Eldjarn, D. Nygaard and S. L. Sveinsson, *Scand. J. Clin. Lab. Invest.*, **7**, 92 (1955).
106 W. H. Horner, *J. Lab. Clin. Med.*, **45**, 951 (1955).
107 A. D. Kenny and S. U. Toverud, *Analyt. Chem.*, **26**, 1059 (1954).
108 N. J. Poulie, *Chem. Weekblad*, **50**, 698 (1954).
109 B. Zak, W. M. Hindman and M. Fisher, *Amer. J. Clin. Pathol.*, **26**, 1081 (1956).
110 R. H. Wilkinson, *J. Clin. Pathol.*, **10**, 126 (1957).
111 H. J. Claes, K. de Doncker and N. Roselle, *Chem. Weekblad*, **55**, 39 (1959).
112 B. Zak, W. M. Hindman and E. S. Baginski, *Analyt. Chem.*, **28**, 1661 (1956).
113 H. M. C. Robinson and J. C. Rathbun, *Canad. J. Biochem. Physiol.*, **37**, 225 (1959).
114 H. V. Malmstadt and T. P. Hadjiioannou, *Clin. Chem.*, **5**, 50 (1959).

115 N. A. Ramaiah, Vishnu and R. K. Chaturvedi, *Naturwissenschaften*, **45**, 290 (1958).
116 H. V. Malmstadt and T. P. Hadjiioannou, *J. Agric. Food Chem.*, **7**, 418 (1959).
117 G. Schwarzenbach, *Complexometric Titrations* (translated by H. Irving), Methuen, London, 1957, p. 36.
118 P. Karsten, H. L. Kies, H. Th. J. van Engelen and P. de Hoog, *Analyt. Chim. Acta*, **12**, 64 (1955).
119 R. Belcher, R. A. Close and T. S. West, *Talanta*, **1**, 238 (1958).
120 I. M. Bett and G. P. Fraser, *Clinica Chim. Acta*, **4**, 346 (1959).
121 E. Stengel and G. Riemer, *Z. analyt. Chem.*, **167**, 118 (1959).
122 N. A. Ramaiah and Vishnu, *Analyt. Chim. Acta*, **16**, 569 (1957).
123 J. P. Riley, *Analyt. Chim. Acta*, **21**, 317 (1959).
124 W. M. Hoffman and H. Shapiro, *J. Ass. Off. Agric. Chem. Wash.*, **37**, 966 (1954).
125 *Official Methods of Analysis*, 7th Ed., Association of Official Agricultural Chemists, 1950, pp. 3, 32, 33.
126 W. A. C. Campen, L. J. H. Nijst and P. J. Neis, *Chem. Weekblad*, **51**, 945 (1955).
127 J. Sneddon, *Brit. Cast Iron Res. Ass. J. Res. & Development*, **7**, 885 (1959).
128 H. V. Malmstadt and T. P. Hadjiioannou, *Analyt. Chim. Acta*, **19**, 563 (1958).
129 L. Aconsky and M. Mori, *Analyt. Chem.*, **27**, 1001 (1955).
130 J. H. Carpenter, *Limnology and Oceanography*, **2**, 271 (1957).
131 H. V. Malmstadt and T. P. Hadjiioannou, *J. Amer. Wat. Wks. Ass.*, **51**, 411 (1959).
132 T. Kanie, *Japan Analyst*, **6**, 711 (1957).
133 A. L. Underwood, *Analyt. Chem.*, **25**, 1910 (1953).
134 H. Flaschka and A. Soliman, *Z. analyt. Chem.*, **158**, 254 (1957).
135 H. Flaschka and A. Soliman, *Z. analyt. Chem.*, **159**, 30 (1957).
136 W. G. Boyle and R. J. Robinson, *Analyt. Chem.*, **30**, 958 (1958).
137 S. Musha and K. Ogawa, *Japan Analyst*, **8**, 161 (1959).
138 A. Dewald, *Acad. rep. populare Romine, Baza cercetari Stiint. Timisoara, Studii cercetari stiint., Ser. I*, **5**, 125 (1958).
139 A. L. Underwood, *Analyt. Chim. Acta*, **20**, 228 (1959).
140 H. Specker, H. Hartkamp and E. Jackwerth, *Z. analyt. Chem.*, **163**, 111 (1958).
141 J. B. Headridge, *Analyst*, **85**, 379 (1960).
142 W. J. Boyer, *Industr. Engng. Chem. (Anal.)*, **10**, 175 (1938).
143 L. D. Brake, W. M. McNabb and J. F. Hazel, *Analyt. Chim. Acta*, **17**, 314 (1957).
144 C. N. Reilley and C. M. Crawford, *Analyt. Chem.*, **27**, 716 (195 5).
145 E. A. C. Crouch and I. G. Swainbank, *A.E.R.E. Report* C/R, 2843 (1959).
146 J. Körbl and R. Pribil, *Chem. Anal.*, **45**, 102 (1956).
147 J. S. Fritz and D. J. Pietrzyk, *Analyt. Chem.*, **31**, 1157 (1959).
148 S. J. Gedansky and L. Gordon, *Analyt. Chem.*, **29**, 566 (1957).
149 G. W. C. Milner and G. W. Sneddon, *A.E.R.E. Report* C/R, 1740 (1955).
150 G. W. C. Milner and G. A. Barnett, *A.E.R.E. Report* C/R, 1865 (1956).
151 C. V Banks and R. E. Edwards, *Analyt. Chem.*, **27**, 947 (1955).
152 S. Musha and K. Ogawa, *J. Chem. Soc. Japan, Pure Chem. Sect.*, **78**, 1686 (1957).
153 H. Hartkamp, *Z. analyt. Chem.*, **171**, 262 (1959).

154 T. L. MARPLE, G. MATSUYAMA and L. W. BURDETT, *Analyt. Chem.*, **30**, 937 (1958).
155 G. W. C. MILNER and G. W. SNEDDON, *A.E.R.E. Report* C/R, 1654 (1955).
156 G. W. C. MILNER and G. A. BARNETT, *Analyt. Chim. Acta*, **14**, 414 (1956).
157 J. BRANDSTETR and S. KOTRLY, *Chem. Listy*, **50**, 1316 (1956).
158 J. CIHALIK and J. NOVAK, *Chem. Listy*, **50**, 1193 (1956).
159 R. WICKBOLD, *Angew. Chem.*, **65**, 159 (1953).
160 R. P. HOLLINGWORTH, *Analyt. Chem.*, **29**, 1130 (1957).
161 R. B. FISCHER, M. L. YATES and M. M. BATTS, *Analyt. Chim. Acta*, **20**, 501 (1959).
162 M. BOBTELSKY, *Heterometry*, Elsevier, Amsterdam, 1960, p. 6.
163 M. BOBTELSKY and J. M. E. GOLDSCHMIDT, *Bull. Res. Council Israel*, **7A**, 121 (1958).
164 M. BOBTELSKY and I. BAR-GADDA, *Analyt. Chim. Acta*, **9**, 446 (1953).
165 M. BOBTELSKY and I. BAR-GADDA, *Analyt. Chim. Acta*, **9**, 525 (1953).
166 M. BOBTELSKY and A. BEN-BASSAT, *Analyt. Chim. Acta*, **14**, 344 (1956).
167 M. BOBTELSKY and R. RAFAILOFF, *Analyt. Chim. Acta*, **16**, 488 (1957).
168 M. BOBTELSKY and M. M. COHEN, *Analyt. Chim. Acta*, **20**, 1 (1959).
169 M. BOBTELSKY and B. CARMON, *Analyt. Chim. Acta*, **21**, 515 (1959).
170 M. BOBTELSKY and R. RAFAILOFF, *Analyt. Chim. Acta*, **17**, 267 (1957).
171 M. BOBTELSKY and I. BAR-GADDA, *Analyt. Chim. Acta*, **9**, 168 (1953).
172 M. BOBTELSKY and J. EISENSTADTER, *Analyt. Chim. Acta*, **14**, 89 (1956).
173 M. BOBTELSKY and B. GRAUS, *J. Amer. Chem. Soc.*, **77**, 1990 (1955).
174 M. BOBTELSKY and E. JUNGREIS, *Analyt. Chim. Acta*, **12**, 248 (1955).
175 M. BOBTELSKY and E. JUNGREIS, *Analyt. Chim. Acta*, **12**, 263 (1955).
176 M. BOBTELSKY and I. BAR-GADDA, *Bull. Soc. Chim. Fr.*, 687 (1953).
177 M. BOBTELSKY and Y. WELWART, *Analyt. Chim. Acta*, **10**, 459 (1954).
178 M. BOBTELSKY and Y. WELWART, *Analyt. Chim. Acta*, **10**, 464 (1954).
179 M. BOBTELSKY and B. GRAUS, *Analyt. Chim. Acta*, **11**, 253 (1954).
180 M. BOBTELSKY and E. JUNGREIS, *J. Inorg. Nuclear Chem.*, **3**, 38 (1956).
181 M. BOBTELSKY and E. JUNGREIS, *Analyt. Chim. Acta*, **13**, 449 (1955).
182 M. BOBTELSKY and J. BLUM, *Analyt. Chim. Acta*, **15**, 62 (1956).
183 M. BOBTELSKY and R. RAFAILOFF, *Analyt. Chim. Acta*, **14**, 558 (1956).
184 M. BOBTELSKY and I. BAR-GADDA, *Bull. Soc. Chim. Fr.*, 276 (1953).
185 M. BOBTELSKY and J. EISENSTADTER, *Analyt. Chim. Acta*, **20**, 216 (1959).
186 M. BOBTELSKY and J. EISENSTADTER, *Analyt. Chim. Acta*, **17**, 579 (1957).
187 M. BOBTELSKY and J. EISENSTADTER, *Bull. Soc. Chim. Fr.*, 708 (1957).
188 M. BOBTELSKY and J. EISENSTADTER, *Analyt. Chim. Acta*, **16**, 479 (1957).
189 M. BOBTELSKY and J. SHAMIR, *Bull. Soc. Chim. Fr.*, 1569 (1958).
190 M. BOBTELSKY and E. JUNGREIS, *Analyt. Chim. Acta*, **12**, 351 (1955).
191 M. BOBTELSKY and A. BEN-BASSAT, *Analyt. Chim. Acta*, **21**, 411 (1959).
192 M. BOBTELSKY and B. GRAUS, *Bull. Res. Council Israel*, **IV**, 69 (1954).
193 M. BOBTELSKY and B. GRAUS, *J. Amer. Chem. Soc.*, **75**, 4172 (1953).
194 M. BOBTELSKY and B. GRAUS, *Analyt. Chim. Acta*, **9**, 163 (1953).
195 M. BOBTELSKY and R. RAFAILOFF, *Analyt. Chim. Acta*, **16**, 321 (1957).
196 M. BOBTELSKY and Y. WELWART, *Analyt. Chim. Acta*, **10**, 156 (1954).
197 M. BOBTELSKY and E. JUNGREIS, *Bull. Soc. Chim. Fr.*, 1161 (1955).
198 M. BOBTELSKY and E. JUNGREIS, *Analyt. Chim. Acta*, **12**, 562 (1955).
199 M. BOBTELSKY and E. JUNGREIS, *Analyt. Chim. Acta*, **13**, 72 (1955).
200 M. BOBTELSKY and R. RAFAILOFF, *Analyt. Chim. Acta*, **14**, 339 (1956).
201 M. BOBTELSKY and R. RAFAILOFF, *Analyt. Chim. Acta*, **14**, 247 (1956).

202 M. Bobtelsky and J. Eisenstadter, *Analyt. Chim. Acta*, **18**, 534 (1958).
203 M. Bobtelsky and I. Yulius, *Analyt. Chim. Acta*, **16**, 75 (1957).
204 M. Bobtelsky and Y. Welwart, *Analyt. Chim. Acta*, **9**, 281 (1953).
205 M. Bobtelsky and Y. Welwart, *Analyt. Chim. Acta*, **9**, 374 (1953).
206 M. Bobtelsky and I. Bar-Gadda, *Bull. Soc. Chim. Fr.*, 819 (1953).
207 M. Bobtelsky and B. Mayer, *Analyt. Chim. Acta*, **15**, 164 (1956).
208 M. Bobtelsky and B. Mayer, *Analyt. Chim. Acta*, **15**, 373 (1956).
209 M. Bobtelsky and J. Eisenstadter, *Analyt. Chim. Acta*, **20**, 352 (1959).
210 M. Bobtelsky and R. Rafailoff, *Bull. Res. Council Israel*, **6A**, 247 (1957).
211 M. Bobtelsky and J. Eisenstadter, *Analyt. Chim. Acta*, **17**, 503 (1957).
212 M. Bobtelsky and J. Eisenstadter, *Analyt. Chim. Acta*, **14**, 186 (1956).
213 M. Bobtelsky and A. Ben-Bassat, *Bull. Soc. Chim. Fr.*, 233 (1958).
214 M. Bobtelsky and A. Ben-Bassat, *Bull. Soc. Chim. Fr.*, 180 (1958).
215 M. Bobtelsky and A. Ben-Bassat, *Bull. Soc. Chim. Fr.*, 1138 (1958).
216 M. Bobtelsky and I. Bar-Gadda, *Bull. Soc. Chim. Fr.*, 382 (1953).
217 M. Bobtelsky and B. Graus, *J. Amer. Chem. Soc.*, **76**, 1536 (1954).
218 M. Bobtelsky and B. Graus, *Bull. Res. Council Israel*, **III**, 82 (1953).
219 M. Bobtelsky and M. Halpern, *Analyt. Chim. Acta*, **11**, 84 (1954).
220 M. Bobtelsky and M. Halpern, *Analyt. Chim. Acta*, **11**, 188 (1954).
221 M. Bobtelsky and R. Rafailoff, *Analyt. Chim. Acta*, **15**, 457 (1956).
222 M. Bobtelsky and L. Bihler, *Analyt. Chim. Acta*, **10**, 260 (1954).
223 M. Bobtelsky and S. Kertes, *J. Appl. Chem.*, **4**, 419 (1954).
224 M. Bobtelsky and S. Kertes, *J. Appl. Chem.*, **5**, 125 (1955).
225 M. Bobtelsky and S. Kertes, *J. Appl. Chem.*, **5**, 675 (1955).
226 A. Ringbom, *Z. analyt. Chem.*, **122**, 263 (1941).
227 H. Frey, *Z. analyt. Chem.*, **133**, 328 (1951).
228 W. W. Brandt and A. A. Duswalt, *Analyt. Chem.*, **30**, 1120 (1958).
229 Y. Y. Lur'e and E. M. Tal, *Zavodskaya Lab.*, **11**, 788 (1945).
230 P.-S. T'ien and K. Wang, *Acta Chim. Sinica*, **25**, 85 (1959).
231 S. Hirano, *J. Soc. Chem. Ind. Japan*, **41**, Suppl. binding 266 (1938).
232 E. Bovalini and M. Piazzi, *Ann. Chim. (Italy)*, **49**, 1067 (1959).
233 H. Frey, *Analyt. Chim. Acta*, **6**, 28 (1952).
234 H. Zimmermann, *Angew. Chem.*, **71**, 336 (1959).
235 C. J. van Nieuwenburg and B. F. Engelbert van Bevervoorde, *Analyt. Chim. Acta*, **19**, 32 (1958).
236 M. Miura and T. Nagakane, *J. Chem. Soc. Japan, Pure Chem. Sect.*, **80**, 53 (1959).
237 H. Frey, *Z. analyt. Chem.*, **132**, 276 (1951).
238 J. M. Lambert, *J. Colloid Sci.*, **2**, 479 (1947).
239 L. D. Goodhue, *Industr. Engng. Chem. (Anal.)*, **10**, 52 (1938).
240 D. R. Morey and J. W. Tamblyn, *J. Appl. Phys.*, **16**, 419 (1945).
241 A. Oth, *Bull. Soc. Chim. Belg.*, **58**, 285 (1949).
242 I. Harris and R. G. J. Miller, *J. Polym. Sci.*, **7**, 377 (1951).
243 J. Bischoff and V. Desreux, *Bull. Soc. Chim. Belg.*, **60**, 137 (1951).
244 H. W. Melville and B. D. Stead, *J. Polym. Sci.*, **16**, 505 (1955).
245 F. Krasovec, N. Vene and A. Peterlin, *Reps. "J. Stefan" Inst.*, **4**, 165 (1957).
246 S. A. Kibardin and T. N. Davydova, *Lab. Delo*, **3**, 3 (1957).
247 M. L. Nichols and B. H. Kindt, *Analyt. Chem.*, **22**, 785 (1950).
248 R. Mavrodineanu and J. Gwirtsman, *Contr. Boyce Thompson Inst.*, **18**, 181 (1955).
249 T. S. Ma and J. Gwirtsman, *Analyt. Chem.*, **29**, 140 (1957).

250 J. Gwirtsman, R. Mavrodineanu and R. R. Coe, *Analyt. Chem.*, **29**, 887 (1957).
251 A. L. Conrad, J. K. Evans and V. F. Gaylor, *Analyt. Chem.*, **31**, 422 (1959).
252 A. C. D. Newman, *Analyt. Chim. Acta*, **19**, 471 (1958).
253 J. A. Dean, M. H. Buehler and L. J. Hardin, *J. Ass. Off. Agric. Chem.*, **40**, 949 (1957).
254 S. Musha and T. Higashino, *Japan Analyst*, **7**, 156 (1958).
255 E. N. Wise, P. W. Gilles and C. A. Reynolds, *Analyt. Chem.*, **25**, 1344 (1953).
256 G. W. Everett and C. N. Reilley, *Analyt. Chem.*, **26**, 1750 (1954).
257 N. H. Furman and A. J. Fenton, *Analyt. Chem.*, **28**, 515 (1956).
258 H. V. Malmstadt and C. B. Roberts, *Analyt. Chem.*, **28**, 1412 (1956).
259 H. V. Malmstadt and C. B. Roberts, *Analyt. Chem.*, **28**, 1884 (1956).
260 H. V. Malmstadt and C. B. Roberts, *Analyt. Chem.*, **27**, 741 (1955).
261 E. N. Wise, P. W. Gilles and C. A. Reynolds, *Analyt. Chem.*, **26**, 779 (1954).
262 A. Liberti, *Analyt. Chim. Acta*, **17**, 247 (1957).
263 J. W. Miller and D. D. DeFord, *Analyt. Chem.*, **29**, 475 (1957).
264 M. Munemori, *Talanta*, **1**, 110 (1958).
265 S. Bruckenstein, *Analyt. Chem.*, **31**, 1757 (1959).
266 E. L. Pratt, *J. Amer. Pharm. Ass.* (*Sci. Ed.*), **46**, 724 (1957).

AUTHOR INDEX

SUBJECT INDEX